WOODSTOCK ANTHOLOGY
(The First Hundred Years)

by
Kyran M. McGrath

Illustrations by
Liz Boyd

Introduction by
Rhoda Walker Teagle

© Kyran M. McGrath 1980

ii

Introduction

Woodstock, Vermont, has remained virtually unchanged for almost two centuries, although many thousands of people have passed through the doors of its white clapboard and red brick houses during these years. The town has had its share of famous people, yet a stranger senses that they were not the ones responsible for the pervasive atmosphere a person feels when walking along its streets and over its bridges. Residents and tourists alike become aware of an ongoing mood, no doubt created by the courage and strength of the earlier inhabitants, their industry, their neighborliness, and their ingenious ability to live through the fiendish winters.

Happily, these qualities have been transmitted to generations born to Woodstock or otherwise choosing to live in its embrace.

A few histories of Woodstock have been published, each quite different from the other. Kyran McGrath, with this volume, has contributed yet another view of older days. He has chosen an array of early settlers and presented them in anthological form. Though not a Vermonter, the author has exhibited an uncanny ability to bring these people to life. No doubt he has been aided by his careful research and endless travels in America. He feels as if the doors of Woodstock's houses had opened to him, and the streets and sidewalks peeled back to reveal the years of footsteps, of conversations, of human nature that had passed before any of us alive today arrived on the scene.

So real is Kyran McGrath's portraiture, that every reader will need time to return to the present after these remembrances of Woodstock people. These pages reflect the joys, the sorrows, the sensitive reactions to life in Woodstock during its first 100 years. When the reader turns the last page of WOODSTOCK ANTHOLOGY, he will have taken a wonderful visit to our past.

Rhoda Walker Teagle
Woodstock, Vermont

Dedication

I dedicate this book to my wife, Rosemary. Without her tolerance and patience I would not have foreseen the sheltered time so essential to start and finish this project.

To my children, my eternal gratitude for being so frank, honest, loving and helpful. Murray and Eileen were away at college when I began, and they would pour over my characterizations while home on vacation. Tom and Roseann, who were on hand in high school at Woodstock, gave me that necessary initial impetus into the subject matter.

My love for reading and my undaunted search for the ironic and delight in life is due to the life-long and wonderful example of my parents, George and Annabelle McGrath. Their observations and opinions on the daily lives they touch in Washington, D.C. are ready material for fiction and current-event writers alike. I wish they would allow us to tape their conversations and share their wit and charm with the world.

Preface

Have you wondered why people settled in Vermont? During the infancy of our nation, it was claimed alternatively by New York and New Hampshire, with neither side winning the argument. Better still, have you thought about the day-to-day life of those early settlers? Some may have lived in huts; others arrived with families. What did they do for doctors; who made their clothes; what attracted them to move away from civilization, or did they bring it with them? Woodstock is one of the most charming villages in New England, but it wasn't always that way. Other people had written about Woodstock, so I decided to search for the answers.

When we moved to Vermont on a full time basis, 1976, we transferred our two younger children, Tom and Roseann, into the Woodstock Union High School. As sort of a patriotic gesture (we billed our move from Washington, D.C. as our family's bicentennial project), I thought the least we could do would be to learn about the town, who settled it, who ran it, what made it tick, what influenced its economic and social movement. Moving into a new area, it is interesting and helpful to know these things.

My first visit to the Norman Williams Public Library brought me face to face with the mystique, the lure of Woodstock. Vivian Bates, then librarian, and Virginia Christy, her successor, introduced me to shelves of material on the subject. They both proved to be walking encyclopedias of the recorded history on Woodstock. My casual interest grew into an embryonic obsession, and soon I was flipping the pages back and forth in Henry Swan Dana's monumental *History of Woodstock, Vermont*, tracking family progressions and tracing ownership of farms, of buildings, locations of burying grounds and churches. Often, I had to leave and pick up Tom and Roseann from their soccer and field hockey practices. Besides, the library would be closing.

The next day, I would be back at the library pouring through more of Dana's invaluable recordings. I cross-checked his information against local newspapers of the era. For a person who had spent seven years in the museum profession, I was thrilled to conduct my research with the original editions, so readily available at the library and just down the street in the historical society.

Dates, events, names, all began to take on delightfully human overtones. By mid-afternoon, I began to imagine how it must have been to have lived one hundred or two hundred years ago, to have felt the joys, the hardships, successes, failures and sharing of local and national events with the neighbors. Who were those people, and what did they think about it at the time it was happening?

After that first week, I presumed to be on friendly terms with many of the historical characters of Woodstock. Exciting? Certainly, but very lonely. I wanted to share my knowledge, but I didn't know who to tell. Someone else might be able to go up to a stranger and say, "Hello, did you know that Solomon Woodward built the stone mill house where the New Woolhouse Players put on their plays, and that after making a fortune, his wife died and he went bankrupt, and he died heartbroken?" I couldn't function on such a frontal attack. Instead, I began to write down characterizations of the people I was reading about, weaving in events and dates that were taking place when they lived, and that obviously played a role and had some influence on their lives. I wrote about the important and the not-so important people of early Woodstock, the people who lived, toiled, laughed, cried, preached, taught, danced, who fought, farmed, tanned, nursed and died in Woodstock. Human nature has been the same for hundreds, thousands of years, and the lives of these forerunners of Woodstock have certainly contributed in their large or small way to the genetic pool that now exists around the Green.

With the nervousness of the untried author, I carried the first 18 or 20 characterizations to Wayne Thompson, a delightful actor with the New Woolhouse Players and who had played in one of my one-act plays. Wayne, exhibiting his wry humor and zest for dramatic interpretation, urged me to write up more characters and bring additional events and years out of the past and into this kind of focus. Both of us are insufferable hams when it comes to local theatre, and I know we were already picking out favorite parts we could play to a hushed, expectant audience.

As days counted into weeks, I wrote more, studied more, and finally gathered my courage to venture into more critical evaluation. John McDill had been described to me as the terrifying, literary mogul who had to be consulted on such aspects of Woodstock history. He proved to be a tower of knowledge, support and encouragement. Fortunately, my wife was at my side for moral and physical support as I stood outside the door of his lovely home. Not only was I frightened of his reknown, intellectual ferocity, I had recently learned that his wife, Mrs. Julia Billings McDill, was the grand daughter of the famous Frederick Billings, about whom I had the audacity to write. To their credit, to my relief, and to our enjoyment, the McDills proved to be very gracious in their hospitality. And they were interested in what I had prepared. They read my characterizations, I answered their questions as best I could, a suggestion here and there, and the visit turned into one of the most enjoyable meetings I had

had in years. In subsequent meetings, John McDill told me of the burden I had placed on him, to review and note changes that were merited here and there, without over-influencing the delicate vulnerability of the author and thus destroy his creative process. He risked this when he taught English at Yale in years past, and he risked it with me. I was flattered to be invited back for more sessions, and I left each time with inspiration and firm resolve to finish, to let the characters mature in my mind and on paper, and then review them again.

Meanwhile, Wayne Thompson introduced me to Liz Boyd, a young Woodstock artist known for her unique line drawings and highly stylized sculpture forms. We three discussed the ideas and impressions I was trying to communicate to the reader. Hopefully, the characters would breach for an hour or two the multi-generation gap that deprived the younger generation of the fun of history and much of the pride of home town life. With the exception of two people, Fr. Neil Cahill S.J. at Campion Jesuit High School, and Dr. Wilkinson at Georgetown University, I had always thought history teachers to be pretty dull, and the subject itself to be as boring as tired quiche. They managed to bring historical characters to life in their classrooms. I have always been grateful. After a couple of meetings, Liz retired to her drawing board.

Weeks went by. When she resurfaced, she presented a number of drawings that depicted events with a visual interpretation I could not begin to match with the written word. I fell in love with them. They conveyed the irony, the happiness, the tragedy I was trying to achieve through my characters. Indeed, they strengthened them. I wrote more; she drew more. Finally, we called it to an end, and I put the material into final review and moved the project into the mendacities that preceed publication.

I hope the reader enjoys this book. It attempts to present life as it took place during the first one hundred years or so of Woodstock's existence. I hope people will feel a kindred spirit with those who came before. With the exception of the Corwin series on vampires (1830), that I suspect cannot be confirmed, the names, dates, places and events are true. The Corwin episode appears in so many recent works on Woodstock, that it is now, if not originally, indeed a part of its history. And anyway, I could not resist including it.

I stayed within the first one hundred years of the village's history for two basic reasons. First, I began with the first settler, and by the end of the civil war, I was simply running out of steam. Second, with many descendants of the characters still alive and very much on the scene at Woodstock, one hundred years over the dam provides a reasonable cushion to allow some literary delving without undue exposure to personal reaction or pressure to include more recently deceased relatives. Besides, I wanted to complete this book and see it in dramatic production.

These characters seek dramatic presentation. Risking audience rejection for the success of applause is one of the challenges posed by this book. Intentionally, I have avoided listing stage directions, character highlights and other dramatic suggestions. Preferably, each director will conceive staging emphasis and apply the creative touch that is so important to cast and audience alike. Having directed a number of plays on an amateur level, I treasure such elbow room for dramatic expression. I think others will also.

Kyran M. McGrath
Plymouth, Vermont

Table of Contents

Table of Illustrations

Woodstock Anthology

1761, GOVERNOR BENNING WENTWORTH

Being governor of New Hampshire,
Under appointment of King George,
I enjoyed some privileges of authority.
I understood, for example,
That the land along the Water Quechee,
West of the Connecticut River,
Had no redeeming value.
Even the Indians did not want it.
So, being governor of New Hampshire,
I claimed the land,
Leaving the governor of New York
Sputtering in rage and subsequent
Presumptions of dubious title.
If the truth be known, I did the colonial folk a favor.
Without my bringing order there,
No civilized man would yet be safe in those swamps.
Applying brilliant care and foresight,
I divided the land
Into 202 parcels, six square miles apiece.
I thought I should charge a fee for these shares;
Without some value attached,
People might think them worthless.
One ear of corn per acre, plus some extra produce,
Not much to ask.
And the added shilling?
Well, after all, I was the governor.

1761, ENSIGN RICHARDSON

"Woodstock" they call it. Humph!
Bugs and rain. "Privation" is what I call it.
To this day,
I cannot say why I ever journeyed up that river.
Wind, and frost in the morning to freeze your toes.
Cob webs filled with water,
Enough to drench your legs at every step.
A "spruce hurricane" is what it should be called.
I wonder if there is a Latin translation for that.
They said I'd be the first white man to set foot here.
Well, I say it straight, I gained a double first:
First to come, and first to leave.
How was I to know others would come and stay?
No newspapers, no roads north or south.
Just Indians, cob webs full of water, bugs,
And that damnable frost in the morning.
Little wonder I reported it a "savage spot."
Under the circumstances, wouldn't you?
I hope no one finds out
I was ever here in the first place.

4

1765, IN RE TIMOTHY KNOX

Yes, if you must know, I jilted Timothy Knox.
How was I to know
He would react so immaturely.
Well, it is important for a girl
To be escorted by educated men.
Timothy claimed he had asked me to the dance,
But I had already accepted another, ah, solicitation.
So, instead of fighting for my hand,
As any other boy from Harvard College should have,
Timothy left in a huff
To go exploring up the Connecticut River.
What a lout! What a silly boy.
There I was,
Abandoned on the field of battle between the sexes,
No one fighting for my hand.
And Timothy, choosing "that savage spot"
Along the Water Quechee,
Living like a hermit in some beaver meadow
For three years.
Hmmm, now that I reflect upon it,
I must really have wounded him.

1765, Timothy Knox

When she jilted me, and I use the term loosely,
I had no choice.
I left Harvard and took up exploration.
Traveled west to the Connecticut, then upstream,
In search of desolation.
Along a side river, I arrived at a place
I dubbed Beaver Meadow.
A quaint spot, unknown to humanity,
Just right for me to nurse my jilted masculinity.
So I stayed, and stayed, and stayed longer still.
People asked me, afterwards, what I did there,
Those three years in Beaver Meadow.
Oh, I fished some, hunted enough to stay alive,
Brooded a lot.
Watched the deer every day.
The young fawns had such skinny legs, they would shake
Like a tree turned upside down,
Its trunk supported by nervous sticks
That threatened to snap at the first hint of breeze.
I grew to love the winter, cold as it was.
Spring was lovely.
I don't know if it was the beauty of the early green,
Or the white dots of first blossoms beside the lingering snow,
Perhaps just plain relief from that damned mud.
Summer and Fall, I loved them also.
Only wish I'd had her with me,
So she could enjoy it too.
I learned a lot about myself,
And I thought a lot about her.
Most of all, I suppose,
I learned that pouting is a big bore.

1769, Mrs. James Sanderson

I do not mind a little inconvenience now and then.
But spending the entire winter in a brush hut
Is a bit much.
James introduced me to Woodstock in 1768.
Or did I introduce him? I forget.
We were both pulling the sled, loaded as it was
With all of our worldly possessions,
And our six-week old baby.
They said, years later,
That we were the first family to winter here.
Or was it,
"We were the first family to survive the winter?"
I wanted to tell them that the Indians had been here
For many years before, more that I can imagine.
But, well, some of our friends are so sensitive
About comparing Indians and white people.
But James and I,
We learned what the Indians went through,
And that brought them and us close together.
"Savages?" Lord no. They must have thought us savages,
Bringing our little baby with us
In the beginning of winter.
Now that it is over,
And the three of us have been recorded for posterity,
Believe me, I would never do it again.

1769, JAMES SANDERSON

Folks are not grateful!
You would think, that after me and my wife,
And our six-week old baby,
Struggled through the snows
To be the first settlers to live in this town,
They would declare us "founders" or something.
You would think they would vote us a pension,
So's we could live in a style
That befits our historic contribution to Woodstock.
But no!
You know what they did instead?
They did nothing, for five years. Nothing!
Then, at a town meeting in 1774,
They elected me, and my brother John, "hog-drivers"!
They told me to keep the loose pigs
From rooting up their vegetable gardens.
Me, the founder of civilization in Woodstock, a hog-driver!
In disgust, and to nurse the wound to my pride,
I moved my family first to Hartford,
Then to New Hampshire,
Not returning until 1778.
I figured that would give folks a chance to repent
Their insult to me and my stature.
No sooner had I set foot back in Woodstock, than damnation,
They re-elected me chairman of that dang hog committee!

1771, Sheriff Ebenezer Dike

Now, let's get it right this time.
Captain Rogers, in his expedition
Against the St. Francis Indians, 1759,
Called it the "Wattock Quitchey."
Captain Stevens, while scouting
From Ft. Drummer to No. 4 Crown Point,
Called it "Quarter Quechee."
And Benning Wentworth, while governor of New Hampshire,
And pretending to some legal claim on the land,
Called it "Water Quechee,"
When he issued his charter in 1761.
I take my orders from Governor Dunmore of New York,
And when he said to take a census of Woodstock in 1771,
By God, I set out to take it.
And I made sure I pronounced the name of that river.
I am going to make sure that all of you
Pronounce that name proper-like.
So's you folk and the governor of New York
Say it the same,
It's "Otta Quechee," right?
Well, I thought so.
Those people from New Hampshire,
They always did have difficulty
Pronouncing things proper-like.
Now, let's get on with the report.
I count forty-two people in town,
That includes ten heads of families,
And nineteen under the age of sixteen.
That's not very many.
But it's a start.

1772, JOAB HOISINGTON

Some folks around these parts
Give credit to James Sanderson
For erecting the first dwelling in Woodstock.
Hell, twigs and pine boughs don't count.
Now you take my house.
There's a real first shelter for you:
Cut boards, floors,
Beds proper for Christian people to sleep in.
When I came up from Hartland, 1771,
I selected the best site in the village.
With only forty-two people here then,
It was easy to do.
Did you hear?
Old Fat King George issued us a town patent.
He did it shortly after I arrived,
But word only recently reached here.
Now we're legal.
Now, because lots of settlers
Will be coming this way next summer,
I'm going to fetch myself a taverner's license.
Whatever their reason for coming,
They'll have one thing in common, an intolerable thirst.
I've never wished hardship on anyone,
But I hope that road is good and dusty,
For my new business, of course.

1772, MRS. JOAB HOISINGTON

Who does he think he is?
Just as I get him to finish our house,
The first in Woodstock,
After I have lived for weeks and months
Amongst dust, mice, bugs
Of every imaginable sort,
And rain running into my bed,
As if the roof protected the bushes outside,
Not us folk inside.
Just as the logs were set in place,
And the furniture constructed,
So God in his wisdom could look down
And see a fit house to live in,
Joab applies for a taverner's license.
Well, I told him, and the Good Lord will bear witness,
No liquor will pass the doorstep of my new house!
Let them take their spirits outside, in the saw dust,
With the mice and bugs and rain.
I hope they all tumble into Kedron Brook
And are swept away.
To think, after all I have had to endure,
He wants to serve liquor in my house.
Who does he think he is?

1772, JOAB HOISINGTON

I will rot in hell
Before I ever try to please that woman again!
I pick out a site fit for the governor himself.
I put up the first permanent dwelling in Woodstock,
Just for her,
A dwelling that even Fat King George
Would be proud to sleep in.
I tick up the bedding so's no mice will get in.
I even put on the roof
Tighter than a lid on a honey jar.
I chase out the bugs, kill off the rats,
Plant some corn within reaching distance of the door.
Slope the fireplace wall so's my wife'll toast all winter.
And all she can do
Is call down the wrath and vengence of God.
I swear, I only suggested that travelers
Might want to place to rest
And to quench a hard-earned thirst.
You would think I asked her to butcher new born lambs,
Or throw baby chicks under wagon wheels.
Good God Almighty,
If ever I try to please that woman again,
Strike me dead on the spot
And tie my bones to the roof of my house,
So's they'll rattle some gratitude into that woman.

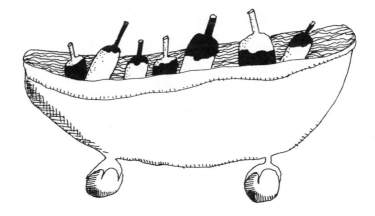

1772, MRS. JOAB HOISINGTON

Humph! I know that man.
Ever since I married him, he only wanted to drink.
I made him the success he is today,
And I did it by keeping the devil and his liquor
Out of our lives.
And Joab?
Well, I suppose he must have developed his evil ways
Before we were married.
But by God, no liquor in my house.
Were I to give in for just one instant,
He'd be soaking his bones in a whiskey jug every day.
I tell you, there's evil floating in that brew.
Spirits will transport a man's mind
And leave him a helpless lump,
And me defenseless in the face of lurking dangers.
No, there'll be no drunkenness in my house,
Husband or no husband.
I've seen what it's done to other folk,
And I've seen where it's left their dependents.
And I've seen that same debauched glint
In the eyes of my Joab.
Oh God, quench the flame of hellish thirst
That burns in his heart, and throat.
Teach him to like tea, or fresh juices.
Help me keep him pure, and temperate. A tavern license,
Humph! I know that man.

1772, JOAB HOISINGTON

My life was a living Inferno,
Until I opened my tavern.
Tea, berry juice, goat's milk.
I was the healthiest of the walking dead.
To convince her of the worthy nature of my proposal,
I told her we'd be doing God's will
By giving traveling folk a shelter,
A place to rest their heads
After coming this far, through lurking dangers.
At night, after all the women folk were asleep,
Including the Misses,
The men, and I of course to serve them,
Would gather in the basement
To quench a long pent-up thirst with whiskey,
Or rum, or well-aged pressings,
Or whatever I could get in store.
I know we were meant to endure a vale of tears
Throughout our lives,
And Lord knows I have had to endure more than most.
But heaven opened her joyful gates to me
The very day I opened that tavern.
Let us pray she never finds out.

1776, REV. AARON HUTCHINSON

While the Constitutional Congress was declaring
Our independence in Philadelphia,
I moved into Woodstock
To tend the spiritual needs of the citizens.
I was known as a Biblical scholar.
I preached to Ethan Allen and his troops
Before the Battle of Bennington,
Rendering them timely inspiration
As my patriotic contribution.
My parish extended far beyond the borders of Woodstock,
And included Pomfret and Hartford as well.
All of the inhabitants, rather limited in that year,
Were members of my parish.
I reminded them of their obligations to God,
And to his chosen ministers on earth.
People credited me with memorizing the Bible;
I accepted this reputation.
When, on occasion, I was caught misquoting a passage,
I was quick to remind the listener
That my memory was of the original Greek,
Not the English translation.

1777, John Darling

I was no hero.
I was not even partially brave.
It was just that Nate Fletcher had a family,
And they could not afford to have him going off to war.
I was only seventeen and unattached,
No wife or children to go hungry if I did not come back.
Seemed only fair that I should go in his place.
Certainly the British would not be able
To tell the difference, that's a fact.
If they shot at me,
I figured I'd have to shoot back,
If that's what was needed to win our freedom from King George.
So I volunteered to serve Mr. Fletcher's draft
In exchange for his equipment,
Enough to set me up in business when I returned.
Figured I could afford to get married then
And gain the responsibilities he had at the time.
That's why I offered to fight the British in his stead.
No hero.
No bravery.
Just common sense.

1777, DR. STEPHEN POWERS

The world is indeed a vale of tears.
When Lydia and I moved to Woodstock,
Two years prior to the War of Independence,
We were very happy, and confident
That nothing could diminish the bounty
Which God himself had showered upon us.
We had five wonderful young children.
I was welcomed as the first medical doctor in town.
To help with the chores,
Because I would be tending to the sick much of the time,
We brought with us our slave, Cato Boston.
I set out for Boston when talk began running strong
About throwing off the British yoke.
Little did I know that soon enough,
I would be dodging musket balls
And dressing wounds at Bunker Hill,
While trying to keep our wounded alive.
I saw my fill of suffering and death at that one battle
To last me a lifetime.
Enough?
Only two years later, I stood helpless
And watched my daughter
Die of the fever.

1778, MRS. PHINEHAS WILLIAMS

The War of Independence took a frightful toll on all of us.
All of us were effected one way or the other.
Phinehas, my husband,
Was captain of one company in the militia,
So naturally he was constantly on call.
This imposed a desperate tension
On our family suppers.
At the town meeting in May, 1775,
Before any formal declaration of war,
The men voted to appropriate funds
For the purchase of gunpowder,
And lead for everyone with flint guns.
That in itself
Seemed to discard loyalty to the King of England.
Then, in July, 1776,
They dealt out powder and lead to all the men.
When General Burgoyne was marching towards Saratoga,
Traveling on the west side of the mountains,
Don't you think Phinehas was the first to rush off,
To help stop Burgoyne from turning east towards Rutland?
Meanwhile, Hezekiah and Roger went out hunting.
By tragic accident, Roger was shot and killed.
I don't blame Hezekiah.
I don't blame Phinehas.
I blame the war.

1779, MRS. BETSY GRAY DOUBLEDAY

We did not get married
Until after the British had surrendered.
Asahel was there when General Burgoyne surrendered.
To think so many people had to be killed,
Just because Burgoyne wanted to hold Saratoga.
I tell you, all of Woodstock was proud that day.
We were proud of Asahel Doubleday.
We were proud of Joab Hoisington
And of Benjamin Emmons and Phinehas Williams.
Oh my, we were so relieved
When news of the surrender reached town.
The messenger raced into the village,
His horse all lathered in sweat,
Shooting his gun into the air to announce the victory.
By nightfall, smoke from the guns discharging lit up the sky.
This caused the village to look more like a battlefield
Than a place of jubilation and thanksgiving.
Oh, there was celebration throughout the new nation in 1779.
Ours lasted for days,
Singing, dancing,
Asahel and me getting married
As soon as he got back from Saratoga.
It's a wonder any of us survived
The victory celebrations.

1785, DANIEL RALPH

Perhaps there is some justification in what they say,
That I am strict in my religious notions.
But when it comes to the way of the Lord,
There must be no deviation.
In 1785, along with Abraham Kendall and Jabex Cottle,
I helped found the Second Baptist Church in Woodstock.
We did it to preserve
The God-fearing ways of our forefathers,
Who had it from the Bible itself,
There was to be no tolerance for the worldly ways
Of sin, and evil, and blasphemy.
Me, my wife, our two children,
We worked hard during every waking hour,
And we managed to held strictly to the Lord's way.
Others should do the same.
I thank heaven I was chosed to be deacon in our church,
I was instrumental in keeping musical tools from defiling
The sanctity of the human voice
Lifted in chorus to God's praise.
I would not even admit the viol into our sanctuary.
The shape of a fiddle, when viewed by the carnal mind,
Could suggest only thoughts of . . . , well,
I would not allow it.
And if that be strict,
Then let them reshape the fiddle.

1787, Captain Israel Richardson

You see, my dear,
They will be more receptive to our proposal
For moving the Windsor Court up here,
If we provide them with the land.
Before anyone else
Begins getting you all worried with loose talk,
I wanted you to hear it first from me,
That we have offered part of our yard
For the new Courthouse.
Now wait, before you say anything,
Listen, please, to why I did it.
First of all,
This will increase the value of the rest of our land.
You see?
Then, because a Courthouse
Is going to bring many important people
To our village, to our property,
We will build a big inn next door,
Also on our property.
Well, those lawyers and judges,
They will have to sleep somewhere.
Oh, and one last thing,
To sweeten the pot just a little bit more,
I said they could use another part of our yard
To put up another building.
I believe they plan to call it a "gaol."

1787, MRS. ISRAEL RICHARDSON

When the Captain, my husband,
Bought our house from the Hoisingtons,
He failed to tell me of his political ambitions.
Just as certain as the winter snows melt in Spring,
And the mosquitos bite in summer,
And the beauty of the leaves
Turns red and scarlet in Fall,
Those men folk can never be satisfied to let things be.
My husband,
No thanks to the importuning of Lawyer Marsh,
Says we ought to bring the court here to Woodstock.
In 1791, the first one would burn,
Only four years old.
For now, they want to take the one from Windsor,
And make Woodstock the shire town for the county.
I swear,
Men can be blind as chickens in a rain storm.

1788, MRS. JOSEPH CHURCHILL

When my husband moved to Woodstock,
Together with his brother, Ichabod,
And when we were married,
We were Congregationalists.
The year our fourth son, Isaac, was born,
We became Baptists.
I wonder why?
For being Baptists,
We owned an unusually successful tavern.
We and the children enjoyed ourselves, and our religion.
At times, I swear, I'll never understand
What gets into men.
They get all fired up about the church,
Argue long hours
Over the differences of religious denominations,
And who should be minister or preacher.
Just when I think all is solved,
And I settle down to try and enjoy the Bible,
We switch to another church.
Maybe it was the baby.
Maybe it was me.
I wonder how long we'll be Baptists?

1791, Mrs. Jerusha West

Praise the Lord for your good health!
That's my message.
Praise the Lord for your good health.
I came to that conclusion after
Giving birth to thirteen children.
I do not attribute my health
To anything I did in the way or prayer
Or other spiritual activity.
No, it is solely up to God
Whether I live or die.
As the number of our children grew, almost yearly,
I got to thinking it must be almost as hard on Elisha
As it was on me.
Funny, his rheumatism
Seemed to get worse with each new baby.
Our poverty increased, too.
Elisha appears to be much the sicker for wear.
That's why I praised the Lord for my good health.
That was all I had left to praise him for.

1791, ELISHA WEST

By the time we moved to Woodstock, in 1791,
We were all accomplished singers.
In fact, back where I came from,
I had the reputation of being chief of the singers.
I would lead the singing,
While my wife had more babies.
I loved every one of our children,
Don't get me wrong.
But thirteen seems to me to be more
Than anyone's fair share.
Maybe it was the singing.
Maybe it was those long Vermont winters.
I got so fretful, I was even afraid
To shake hands with that woman.
I don't know if my poverty,
That I seem to have visited on each
Member of the family,
Is the result of my ignorance or hers,
Or maybe God's way of portioning things out.
If each child in a rich family
Would help thin out their wealth, and so end up poor,
Wouldn't it only seem fair
That each child in a poor family
Would help thin out their poverty, and so end up rich?
Seems logical to me. Hmmm . . .
Maybe I should just stick to singing.

1792, Mrs. Dinal Atheorn Daman

My husband's life as minister had become intolerable!
He did not graduate from Harvard,
Become an ordained minister of the Lord,
Raise our seven children
And move to Woodstock for the purpose of officiating
A dispute over where parish boundaries
And meeting houses should be located.
The controversy, set in motion before our arrival,
And enlarged upon by the contending factions
Once they had his presence to appeal to,
Had only served to "stir local prejudices and rivalries"
Among people who otherwise should be united
By common interests and common hazards of the day.
By 1788, they appealed
To an outside source of expertise.
The referee, applying wisdom descended from Solomon,
At last agreed with both factions, and criticized both.
With neither side budging one step,
But rather seeking recruits for what could inflame
Our members into religious civil war,
My husband tried to concentrate on the Bible.
Were it not for the necessity of securing food,
And fuel and shelter in 1792,
Surely Woodstock would have argued itself to death.

1792, MRS. LYDIA DREW POWERS

I told him it would come to this,
And he would not listen to me.
Now Reverend Daman has aked to be dismissed,
And we are to be left without a preacher,
Without a minister, without a fit scholar
To preach the sermons to us.
It began in 1779, when the town voted
To divide itself into two parishes,
One north, and the other, south.
It grew worse two years later,
When they built the log meeting house
 And immediately began arguing over a better site.
When Reverend Daman and his large family
Arrived that same year,
The seeds of his failure had already been planted.
My husband, the only doctor in town,
Along with Benjamin Emmons and John Strong,
Began agitating
For their choice of a new site for the meeting house.
Reverend Hutchinson, then retired,
But still of great influence,
Aided by many others in the village, assumed a protective
Stand for Reverend Daman, thus drawing the lines of
Ecclesiastical warfare, from which no one could benefit.
Sometimes, the fathers of our village
Act more like Philistines than Pharisees.

1792, TITUS HUTCHINSON

While the good people of Woodstock
Were about to mount congregational bloodshed
Over the issue of where to locate
The meeting house, for the delivery of God's word,
I, being the son of Reverend Hutchinson,
And thereby an informed observer,
Decided to leave town and enter college.
I traveled to Dartmouth, with my clothes packed
For a year's study, with what little provisions
My family could provide.
At Dartmouth, the trustees told me
That I could not enter unless I paid the full tuition
For four years in advance.
That institution was never known to neglect the financial
Recognition of its education.
Being well packed, and intent upon a college degree,
I proceeded southward and enrolled at Princeton,
Where, subsequently, I graduated second in my class.
Many years afterwards, I returned to Woodstock,
And eventually became chief justice
Of the Vermont Supreme Court.
Don't you suppose that I had often wished to hear a case
In which Dartmouth
Might have been sued by one of her students?

34

1793, Nancy Collins Marsh

No matter what Dr. Powers told me,
And despite the prayers and counsel of the minister,
I wished I would have lived
To see my two children grow up,
And to see my husband
Become a successful, acclaimed attorney,
A member of the United States Congress,
And live in that beautiful house he build
Following the turn of the century.
Sad, isn't it,
That the men who are exposed daily
To physical and stressful dangers
Live so much longer than we women?
They can say all they want
About how hard they work in providing for us,
And I am sure they do just that.
Still, bearing their children is harder
And more dangerous.
It kills so many of us.
I had only eight days to live after the birth of my Ann,
Barely enough to know her at all.
And yound Charles, only three years of age,
Could hardly be expected to remember me as he grew up.
Sadly, I died,
After clinging to life those eight precious days.

1793, CHARLES MARSH

Oh God, what more do you want?
Nancy and I kept your commandments.
We saw our duty to you and to our brothers here on earth.
We performed to the extent of our abilities.
Still, you took her away from me,
From young Charles and our new baby, Ann.
Oh God, where is your mercy?
People may hold me in esteem
As the town's first lawyer.
And they may extend their pity
Towards me and the children.
At this moment, they have no idea how tragic,
How helpless,
How undeserving I am of their respect.
I feel no strength.
I see little value in the laws I struggle to defend.
I am even on the verge of denying
A belief in the Biblical justice
Attributed to you.

1796, Mrs. Richmond Tracy

When I held Andrew in my arms,
And nursed him through his first critical months,
I would gaze into his young eyes,
Already so intense and penetrating.
I knew at the time that he would become
A brillant lawyer, or politician, or both.
While I did not live to see all of the legal
And political accomplishments of my son,
I am well informed that indeed,
He went on to become
An outstanding member of the Vermont bar,
Devastating opponents at will,
Using those same penetrating eyes to sway juries
And judges alike.
The state boasted, or suffered,
Three political parties by 1830.
Andrew brought the state National Republican Party
To full power and influence.
He foresook it for the Whig Party in 1834, for good reason.
He applied unparalleled wit and sarcasm in bringing order
To the Vermont Legislature,
Particularly when he served as Speaker
Of the House, from 1842-1844.
Oh, I could go on and on about my boy.
He was born brilliant, and he lived brilliantly.
Please forgive a mother's pride.

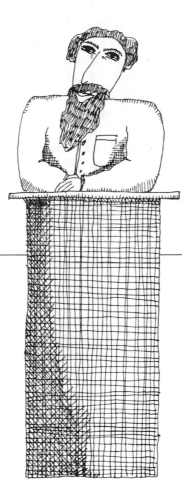

1798, Susan Arnold Marsh

When Charles asked me to marry him,
Five years after her death,
I knew he still loved her.
What man of learning and compassion would not?
But I regarded the matter in this fashion:
Many young people died in 1793, and many died in 1798.
Women during child birth were especially exposed
To the agony of death,
Or the calling of heaven,
However the ministers looked at it.
Charles continues in life, as do his children,
And he wants me to share his life, and theirs.
For his tender years in the legal profession,
He is an accomplished man, one of profound respect.
If I can help him succeed in life,
For the honor of God, of his family,
And even of her, if that be in his mind,
Then surely I would be selfish not to honor his request.
Besides this rational motive,
I willingly confess,
I am deeply in love with him.

1798, JUSTIN MORGAN

It is not fair
That I should die in poverty,
While Sheriff Rice seized my horse
In satisfaction of same paltry debt.
I rode up from Massachusetts,
Teaching school and music along the way.
And my horse?
He was put to hauling logs, plowing,
Racing in cheap, eighty-rod runs
To win jugs of whiskey and gin for a succession of owners.
Marvelous horse!
Strong, gentle as a lamb in the April sun,
Quick as a mink in a chicken coop.
If I had it to do over again,
I'd have worked harder to make him famous
During his lifetime, and mine,
Not let Bob Evans and David Goss hitch him to plows,
Or swagger bets in pulling contests.
The poor horse, kept working 'til he died,
Age twenty-nine.
Another horse kicked him in the ribs,
And no one tended the wound.
Like me, he died in poverty.
Now we're both famous,
Now when it doesn't matter to either of us.

1801, NATHANIEL DUTTON

When I first saw that building,
I told them it was not fit for teaching.
Cattle? Maybe. Hogs? Yes. Horses? I suppose.
But it was definitely not for human occupancy,
Much less learning.
I was informed, categorically,
That school would be taught in there,
Or on some nearby hillside.
Being headmaster of a hillside is not my idea of a career,
So I relented, or accepted, whichever,
Gritted my teeth, held my nose, and did the best I could.
There was little surplus money in 1801
To support formal education,
Or its students, or its headmaster.
So I bowed to the burdens of deprivation,
And determined to instruct the young people of Woodstock.
I hoped they,
By receiving a strong foundation in mathematics, reading,
Understanding of the human spirit,
Would in future years,
Give schools the support we never enjoyed.
Some time later, when I saw our school burning,
I watched with mixed emotion.
Indifferent about the benches, so hard and unmerciful,
I was overjoyed, although I only say this in private,
At seeing the building reduced
To a part of that damn hillside.

1802, MRS. PRISCILLA GRAY

My husband used to tell me
That one of the benefits of living along the Quechee River
Was the opportunity
To harness the energy of the rushing waters,
And to use it for mechanical purposes.
He was mechanical, I wasn't.
So I kept the house,
Grew the vegetables in our short seasons,
Milked the cow, kept weasels from killing the chickens.
Meanwhile, Eben tried his hand at tanning
With his brother, Jabez.
They worked along the river, utilizing those rushing waters,
Just like he said he would.
Seems the only trouble with the whole scheme
Was that Eben could not stand the smell.
So he quit.
Jabez kept the tanning business, such as it was.
And we took to farming, near the east end of Pleasant Street,
With more cows, and chickens, and hogs.
Now, I can't stand the smell.

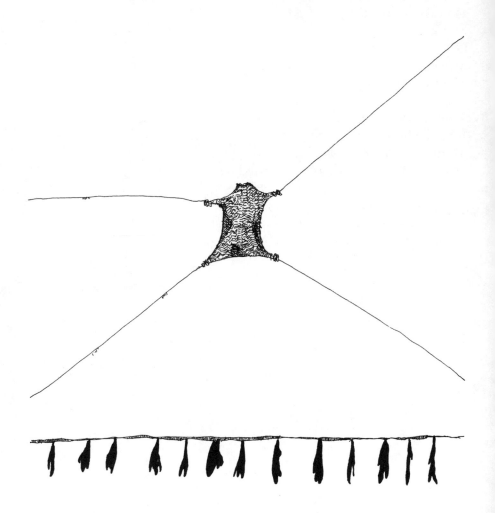

1802, Mrs. Sally Rice

That man should have punched him in the nose,
And I told him so.
Just because my husband is the sheriff
Does not give him an excuse
For scaring people out of their senses.
Can you imagine?
He told Mr. Richardson,
On the morning of April 1st, when else,
While the poor man was shaving,
That his son had been crushed in the mill.
Poor Mr. Richardson ran all the way,
Half lathered from his shave, half dressed,
And half dead from fright and grief,
While Bill and his cronies
Slapped their thighs and laughed
Until tears streamed down their faces.
I don't call that joking.
I call it an invitation to getting your head blown off.
I doubt if a jury could have been found
To convict Mr. Richardson
If he had shot Bill.
My husband's been sheriff for four years now,
And you'd think he'd know better.
I just wish I were a man.
I'd have punched him in the nose.

1804, MRS. PRISCILLA RAYMOND

When my husband died,
I believe the entire county must have wept.
That man had made more people hereabouts
Happy with his fiddle music.
He learned music long before he came to Woodstock.
So, when he arrived, he had played all of the sour notes
Out of his fiddle.
Folks would ask if I minded his being away so often,
Playing at parties, weddings, apple-parings, quiltings.
Heavens no!
I was as happy as he was just to know so many people
Were enjoying themselves.
The fact that he was able to be the cause
Of so much fun and merriment,
Well, I felt proud to have a hand in it,
Keeping his home, fixing his food, mending his clothes,
In general patching him up after work
So's he could bring his music to people.
"Fiddler John" did not have a sorrowful bone in his body,
And I loved him for wanting to share his enjoyment
With other people.
When he died, in 1804,
Most of the tears I shed came from knowing
Folks would not be hearing him play anymore.
During the fifty-three years I lived afterwards
I never felt lonely, or sad, or cheated.
I felt happy, and I felt proud.

1805, STEPHAN DELANO

Never once did I intend to champion
The extravagance of aristocratic wit.
My intelligence bid me aspire to more
Than becoming "a mere farmer."
So I took up the pen, the speaker's platform,
And on occasion, the pulpit and the town hall,
To, ah, extend the benefit of my thoughts
And opinions, for I prized them highly,
And believed others should do likewise.
In religion, I was first a Congregationalist.
By 1782, I joined the United Baptist Society
With my colleagues, Ichabod Churchill and Benjamin Burtch.
Twelve years later, I had gleaned from that society
Every kernel of wisdom,
And I was able to step directly
From the embrace of Calvinistic Baptists
Into the Universalist Church.
True, not many have been able to fathom the nuances
Of such a liturgical circuit, an ecclesiastical progression.
But then, I am well read.
In politics, I was first a Federalist,
An ardent admirer of Washington.
As time moved on, I switched to Republicanism.
Finally, I returned to the bossom of Jeffersonian Democracy.
Well, I found it the only path of salvation for our country.
Besides, religion and politics thrive on the unexpected.

1807, MRS. MARY HARVEY

When I recall how he survived much worse,
I cannot see how he could die like this.
He served under Captain Goldsmith, in the Revolution,
And Lord knows he took his chances
In the service of our young nation.
He took his chances when he moved to Woodstock in 1782,
When there was so much talk of Indians
Coming down from Canada.
I suppose you might say he took his chances
Marrying me the following year.
Well certainly, he risked his life last April,
Crossing over the ice
On the Connecticut River.
How ironic, returning with Nathan
From a simple trip to Hartford,
Just to pay a bill,
He should get swept over Taft's Dam in a canoe.
I heard what the minister said,
And I've read the Bible, time and again.
All that talk about conciliation, and God's mercy.
Oh God, fifty years of dangers,
And you take him away from us
For crossing the river above Taft's Dam.
Why couldn't you let him have it to do over again?
The next time, I'm sure he'd cross below the dam.

1811, URIEL DUTTON

No, I do not say it is the fashion
To burn down schools,
Nor do I make accusations.
I merely point out that it seems strange
For the school house to burn to the ground
Only two weeks before the end of the session,
And immediately before the commencement of examinations.
A similar occurrence happened to Nathaniel's school,
Although he had less love for that building
Than I had for mine.
Nonetheless, I would be derelict in my responsibility
Were I not to point out the peculiar
Pattern that emerges in the burning of school houses
At this time of year.
It has not been dry, rains have been plentiful,
No unusual need for additional heat during class time.
You do not see other buildings burning this season,
Courthouses, distilleries, barns, or inns.
Only school houses.
They are predicting another war with England by a year's end.
Well, I say we are at war right now,
With an enemy of education,
And an enemy of the future of Woodstock.
Without schools, we will see our children,
And their children,
Reduced to the ranks of barbarians and heathen.
The next school we build, let it be of brick.

1811, JAMES CUTLER

The law bored me.
I studied under Charles Marsh, Esquire, for three years,
Cramming torts, common law, and contracts into my head,
Until I began to see musical notes dancing along
The pages of the copius books I was assigned to read.
Maybe I was disenchanted by their dust,
Or the rotting leather in which they were bound,
Or the uncertainty of preference
That a judge might give to either of two
Equally weighted but diametrically opposed arguments.
On the other hand, music enchanted me.
With music, you knew exactly where you were,
Its tempo, its pitch, its harmonics
So beautifully and predictably woven together.
I devoted most of my time to music.
I loved it.
While I kept the public school
In South Village for three years,
You can be certain,
Those young scholars learned to sing as well
As any choir in New England.
Now and then, my students would try to rebel.
But with strict discipline, and encouragement,
I held them to their task,
And they brought glory to the divine art.

1811, DR. JOHN DREW POWERS

People give me credit for being well educated,
A reknown doctor.
When I watched my sister, Susanna, die
I promised myself,
Standing next to her body still steaming from the fever,
That when I grew up,
I would become the best doctor in Vermont,
So I could help other people avoid
The tragic losses I had endured.
Years later, I became a doctor, a very fine doctor,
Given the medical limitations
Of the 19th century.
I learned as much as I could about diseases from Dr. Gallup,
Anatomy, surgery, chemistry, and the biological processes
By which we frail mortals manage to stay alive.
And I was able to help other people avoid tragic losses.
Still, after a life time of devotion
To surgery and medicine,
I watched helplessly as two of my young sons
And my beloved wife, Sally, died of the fever.
Surely I am entitled to feel anger,
To feel outrage,
To feel provoked beyond Christian endurance.
I feel . . . so terribly . . . empty, so hurt,
I feel . . .

1811, MRS. SALLY DREW POWERS

When I married John,
I knew I was marrying into a family
With acclaimed medical heritage.
I knew this would not solve
All of the problems that might arise
During our life together, but I knew it would help.
Then Casper, our first son, died at the age of two.
I remembered that John's father had said,
"The world is indeed a vale of tears."
Next, our second son, Volney, died at the age of ten.
Spotted fever, same as Casper.
Later, sick with the same dread disease,
I knew there was little hope for me.
And there wasn't.
I died too.
Lucky for John, and lucky for Woodstock,
Our two younger sons lived.
I was a God-fearing woman, and a good mother.
But sometimes, I thought that God
Could have distributed his blessings
With a stronger eye on lineage.

1812, Mrs. Lucy Hunter Churchill

Maybe it was my fear about war with the British,
More likely it was love and devotion
That led me to marry Sylvester Churchill.
He was commissioned a lieutenant,
Saw service in 1812 with his brother, Isaac, and his cousins,
Then decided to stay in the Army.
I hesitate to say war has been good to us,
War is never good.
Following his later service in the Mexican War,
Including his survival of the Battle of Buena Vista,
He was promoted to inspector general,
Later to brigadier general.
Many women I know have suffered very much
At the hands of war.
Their husbands, sons, fathers, brothers or loved ones
Come home dead or crippled for life.
I was fortunate, Sylvester was fortunate.
Still, in spite of the personal comforts I have enjoyed
As a result of his service,
I wish there was no need for an army.
But if a nation is rich, as ours is,
And weak, as ours must never be,
It will be attacked by its enemies.
That is why Sylvester joined the army,
And why I married him.

1812, MRS. CLARISSA SAGE HUTCHINSON

I know the wife of a professional man
Should keep a respectful tongue.
But I have just returned from the Common,
Where Titus, my husband,
Was leading the military rejects in parade,
Those men the army would not take in the War of 1812.
Such goings on, I swear.
Titus may be a brilliant lawyer,
And destined to become a leader of his profession.
But his profession suffers
When he and his cronies march around town.
The company is the Washington Patriotic Company,
Commonly called the "Silver Grays,"
After the age showing in their hair.
Being older, and thinking themselves thereby more entitled,
They submit themselves to no one else's authority.
They borrow muskets from other men.
They parade on other than regular training days.
And, they maintain their headquarters on the Common,
In a washtub of brew,
Placed conveniently so's they can drink their valour.
But for the absence of the Churchills,
The Houghtons, the Raymonds and John Sanderson,
We'd hardly know there was a war.
And if those Silver Grays keep parading,
We'd hardly know there was a legal profession.

1814, MRS. RACHEL STILES BREWSTER

Following what seemed to be only a day after our marriage,
Paul enlisted in the service.
He claimed an unholy desire the fight the British.
Those two years without him,
Not knowing from month to month
If he was dead or living, wounded or captured,
Were two years in the Inferno for me.
Paul's family were farmers in South Woodstock.
Fortunately, his father had saved enough before he died,
Four years back, to provide for his widow and children,
And for me.
Paul's grandfather had fought in the French and Indian War,
And had helped Lt. Ransom lay out the road
From the Common to Reading.
I suppose the military was in Paul's bones.
I just prayed for it to get out of our marriage.
Finally, he came back,
Safe, and in one piece.
He may forget the war, and others may claim it is over.
But for me, the nightmare of those two years,
Of daily fear for his life,
Is burned in my mind forever.
Who says women are not involved in war?

1815, JOHN SANDERSON

Before the War of 1812,
I was a member of the Universalist Church.
Then I enlisted,
Along with Ben Richardson and Zebina Raymond.
We saw action together under General Harrison,
At Tippecanoe.
Others from Woodstock were in the war, too:
The Churchill boys, the Houghtons,
Lysander and Barny Raymond,
All good men and brave.
I was no hero,
Although children in town called me that when I returned.
Funny, they never asked me
What I did before I was a soldier,
Thinking, I suppose, that somehow I was born in uniform.
So, I was glad, relieved,
Not to tell them I had been a hog-driver
Along with my brother.
God I hated that work!
Better to be a soldier and risk getting your head shot off,
Than spend your days chasing after peoples' pigs.
Now that I've come home,
My war record should help keep me from
Having to ever chase those damn hogs again.
I might even go back to being a Universalist.

1817, PRESIDENT JAMES MONROE

When I traveled to Vermont in 1817,
While serving as President of the United States,
I thrilled to the sight of mountains and valleys
Cloaked in green forests.
Abundant streams guided waters, crisp and pure,
As they bounced past rocks into rivers
Of pastoral delight.
What relief for a tired politician.
I cannot say if the people there were industrious
Before they arrived,
Or if the necessity of winter survival and mountain farming,
Bred industry into them.
Possibly the weak died off, or moved south
Where a livelihood was less arduously secured.
My day in Windsor County
Left me impressed
With the inner strength of America.
It also reminded me of the scope of responsibilities
For presuming to her presidency.

1817, MEHITABLE MURDOCK HOOPER

Benjamin Swan, Esquire, became State Treasurer in 1800
And was reelected to that post for thirty-two years.
My husband was his carpenter.
Mr. Swan was always mindful of us poor people,
And he saw that help was available when necessary.
I can remember him, Mr. Swan,
Serving on the arrangements committee
For the visit to Woodstock by President Monroe.
Oh, Cyrus and I were so proud of him, Mr. Swan,
For being so important as to arrange the visit
For the President of the United States.
That day, July 23, 1817,
Captain David Mack, company commander of the local calvary,
Rode to Hartford to meet the President.
They all entered town at 10:00 in the morning,
Dismounting to greet the viewers on foot,
And walking to Mr. Pratt's inn, where Mr. Swan and Mr. Marsh
Officially greeted him, the President.
The temptation to speak
Before the President of the United States,
Being too much to resist,
Mr. Hutchinson gave an extended introduction.
Then Mr. Monroe himself spoke, briefly, the time being
Already used up.
Soon, amidst firing of cannons
And cheering from the throng of people,
The President departed,
Heading north through Royalton towards Montpelier.
I was proud of Mr. Swan.
He chose to remember his home town that day,
Rather than stay in Montpelier with more important people
Who also were waiting to greet the President.

1819, MRS. ROBERT BARKER

When Robert bought the Village Hotel, in 1819,
He did it against my sound advice.
That building looked like it was about to tumble down.
No wonder, it'd been built before the turn of the century.
I supposed they called it representational architecture,
Constructed by Elish Taylor.
Big rooms, wide windows, parlors too big to keep warm
Half the year.
If they continue building that way,
There won't be any trees left in Windsor County
By the end of the decade.
Imagine, forty cords of wood needed for heat and cooking
In just one house for the year.
So, against my sound advice,
Robert bought the Village Hotel.
He was getting ready to quit his job
Driving stagecoach between Windsor and Randolph.
Lord, I hope that hotel does not fall down on his head.
Either fall down or burn down,
It's destined for one or the other.
If I was smart, I'd pray for an early grave.
Then I wouldn't have to bear witness to the wisdom of my words.
Besides, Robert hates me to say,
"I told you so."

1819, ROBERT BARKER

I did not buy that hotel for the purpose of making money.
Hell no. I bought it because
I'd been sitting on that stagecoach every week
For as long as I can remember,
Driving eighty miles
In rain, sun, dust, snow, hail, freezing cold,
Bored to death while trying to make a living.
Ever think how lonesome it can get on top of a stagecoach?
Passengers never contemplate
How lonely the driver must feel.
Instead, they complain about ruts in the road, or the cold,
Or the heat in the summer, or the dust most of the time.
A few of them, too cheap to buy their own,
Or too dumb to think ahead,
Even ask me for food and drink.
I knew I'd had enough last week,
When I saw that big oak tree, just passed the river,
Finally crash to the ground.
It had grown proud and tall for easily one hundred years.
People passed it coming and going,
Never giving it a thought.
At first, I used to admire that tree, then I came to love it,
Growing proud and tall, a monarch among trees.
Dammit, when it crashed to earth,
Wearied from so many storms,
People began cutting it up for firewood.
That's when I thought,
"I am just like that oak tree,
And they are cutting me up for firewood."
That's why I bought the Village Hotel.

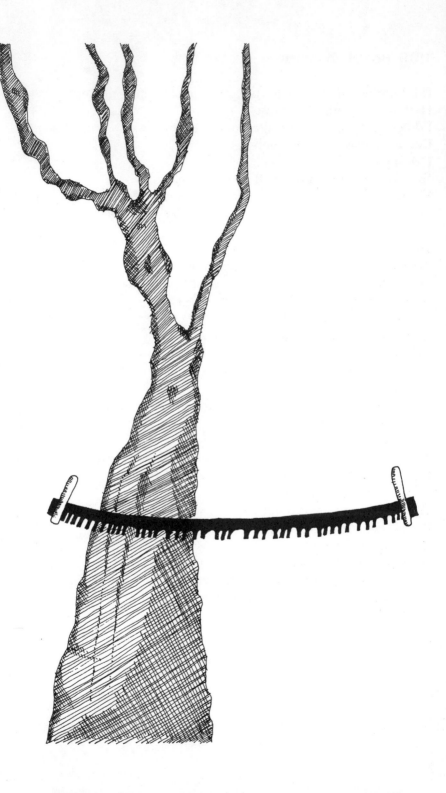

1820, Sylvester Edson

When you do something,
You don't figure at the time
That you'll be recorded in the history books.
Take me for instance.
When I bought that land on Central Street
From Zebina Curtis, back in 1814,
I knew I was going to build something on it.
Otherwise, why buy property in town?
Well, when I built a series of buildings, all in a row,
Six years later,
Little did I know
How the commerce of Woodstock would be effected.
Dry goods, saddlers, jewelry, book binding,
All were shops that moved in.
Even secured a post office to make it official.
I am not saying I became the most important man in town,
But I can say those shops
Became the biggest attraction hereabouts.
Hmm, I wonder if old Zebina ever knew how close he came
To being famous.

1820, MRS. ZEBINA CURTIS

I do not often complain about my Zebina.
But when he sold that property on Central Street
To Sylvester Edson,
I let him know in no uncertain terms
That he was a fool, general or no general.
He could have built those buildings
And made all of that money for ourselves.
Instead, he kept laughing, and saying to himself,
"Old Sylvester's dumber than I thought."
Well, I reminded him that "Old Sylvester" was able
To buy his family new clothes, a beautiful carriage,
One proper to go to church in,
And a position for his wife in Woodstock society.
So I kept at my Zebina,
Wanting him to learn
Not to go throwing opportunity away like that.
About that same time, he took to setting on the porch,
Just watching the hawks and crows flapping in the sky.
In later years,
Despite my continual urgings to do something with himself,
He seemed more content than ever to sit out there
Than to be with me.
He'd listen to the sky, to nothing.
Not a sound, and he seemed so contented.
That man aggravates me so.

1820, GENERAL ZEBINA CURTIS

Sylvester bought my property,
Lying low and dusty along Central Street.
I figured him to be the biggest fool of us all.
Horses, carriages, cattle, squacking geese and chickens
Constantly on parade past that property.
Lord, I could not stand
The infernal racket of that intersection.
There was enough of that in the army.
I returned to Vermont for peace and quiet.
Let the Edsons of the world build their commerce
And go down in the history books.
So, when he built his row of businesses in 1820,
I was not jealous,
Even though folks called me crazy
For not thinking of doing it myself.
No sir, I just sat back and laughed,
Happy to breath the clear air on my porch,
And enjoy the sounds of nature
Along the hillsides north of Windsor.
Ever watch the hawks and crows,
Wild geese in the Spring and Fall,
Glide past the edge of these mountains?
I think of Sylvester raking in all of that money,
And choking on all of that dust,
And listening to the squacking geese and stupid chickens,
And watching someone else's
Cows go to the bathroom on his front steps.

1824, PRISCILLA SMITH TRIBOU

I think it is shocking!
A decent lady
Cannot even rest easy in her grave these days.
Well, don't say I did not always contend,
"You cannot trust people from Connecticut."
There is growing alarm over the "abominable practice
Of disinterring the dead for anatomical purposes."
That is what they wrote in Hartford, in 1824.
And just the other day, in the OBSERVER, I read,
"The public mind
Has been greatly agitated by the disinterment
Of a respectable female in the neighborhood of New Haven,"
You see,
It is always in Connecticut that these things happen,
"Whose body was subsequently found in the Medical Institute
Attached to Yale College."
My family moved up here from Massachusetts,
And believe me,
You would never find that sort of thing going on at Harvard.
Harvard men know how to treat respectable ladies.

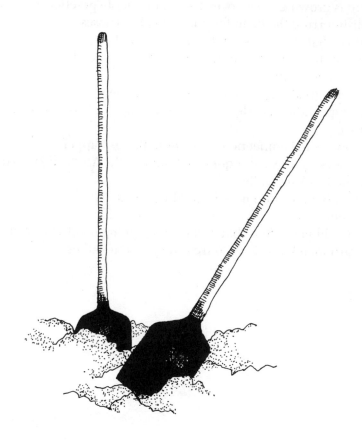

1825, Susan Sylvester

Oh, that was a day to remember!
Proud and tall, he rode into town a true French hero.
His red hair fairly burst from beneath his hat,
As he rode along the Common and stopped before the hotel,
That day, so many years after the Revolutionary War.
Mother, my teachers, in fact the entire village,
Had talked so often of the valiant services
He had rendered on behalf of our young nation
During those first critical months of the War.
Everyone respected and loved General Lafayette.
He helped America win her freedom,
And we were all in his debt.
I was quite young at the time,
So I cannot remember all that he said.
I had learned some French, and he knew some English.
But I can remember that red hair, alive with patriotism,
With love for America and freedom everywhere.
I remember seeing the banquet table that had been prepared
For him, in honor of the War veterans from Woodstock.
The roast pig was crisp, well cooked.
The steam itself was delicious enough to nourish our joy.
And that pig, sitting fat and roasted on the platter,
With a lemon in its mouth,
It being June and no apples on hand,
Reminded me of the King of England.

1827, HANNAH SYLVESTER

I tell you, there is so much going on these days,
A working lady is hard pressed
Just to keep up with the gossip in the village.
My Susan is still excited from seeing General Lafayette.
Wheat farming is dying out around Vermont,
Seems the lands opening up out west are better suited.
I guess sheep will have to suffice,
Although they are stupid as sin on Sunday morning.
I don't know if I like the idea of that new medical school
Opening in the village.
You know the talk of where those students
And their teachers get bodies for practice.
We may not have many scientific advancements in 1827,
But we have our dignity,
And we have our rights of privacy, in life and in death.
I tell you, I don't want any medical student digging me up
And poking around with his surgical blades. The very idea!
It is not easy raising children these days,
But I will work my fingers to the bone
To provide a safe grave for them and me.
Oh my, and so many people dropping dead from the fever.
There is just too much happening these days.

1828, Mrs. Cyrus Clement

My husband was a tanner,
Operating along the Quechee River.
In fact, you might say he operated over the Quechee River.
At least he operated over a brook that fed into it.
I told him it was not safe
To build a barn over that stream,
Much less one with our house attached to it.
But he went ahead, and we sat there,
Vulnerable to flood waters,
Like a chicken nest under a water pump, sort of.
I don't think I would have minded
If just the barn
And the stinking tannery in it were to wash away.
But when the flood hit, while we were asleep of course,
The waters reached up to the barn from underneath,
Threatening to sweep the entire building down river.
We woke to the sound of raging waters outside
And creaking timbers inside.
Water covered the rugs and made islands of the furniture.
Cy rushed outside for help, while I gathered the children.
We managed to survive, thanks to our neighbors.
No thanks at all to my husband.
We tied the building to some trees,
Like a fat boat in an angry lake.
And on his birthday,
I gave my husband a big oar, just in case.

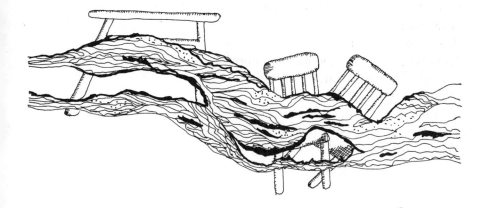

1828, Cyrus Clement

Have you ever worked in a tannery?
Let me tell you, it is hard business.
Wetting hides of all sizes and shapes,
Scraping off the dried fat, and blood,
And other obnoxious tissue after the lime bath.
Next comes the long soaking with crushed oak bark.
God knows, it's messy.
But it is essential to lots of people in Vermont.
Naturally, I was upset when my wife kept after me
About building our barn over the brook
Leading into the Quechee River.
I swear, I told her I built it there so we could
Get all the water we needed for washing,
And treating,
And soaking the hides.
Her complaining made me mad enough.
Imagine how mad I felt that night
When the flood waters rose up
And lifted my barn right off its foundation?
That flood proved all along that I was wrong.
Worse still, it proved that she was right.

1828, MRS. MARGERY BREWSTER

Some folks carry religion a bit too far.
Take Dick Ransom for example.
He would not tolerate the most harmless form of entertainment,
Claiming it violated the message of God
As set forth in the Bible.
One night, during the midnight ball at Richardson's Hotel,
Dick showed up all full of wrath and God's vengence,
Intent on dragging his grand-daughter away
From the "mixed assembly"
He claimed was the certain road to sin and perdition.
I was there,
Widowed eighteen years but delighting in the music
And the sight of so many happy people.
And in came old Dick Ransom,
Crying down God's calamity on the lot of us.
Chivalry was still alive,
And some young men spirited
His terrified grand-daughter out of sight.
She stayed with relatives
Until he'd allow her back in his house.
Sure as sunlight allows us to see the beauty of life,
God meant for us
To enjoy an innocent dance from time to time.
I told Dick afterwards,
"Even God allowed his own son to attend a wedding feast."

1829, ABRAHAM STEARNS

George Rice woke me up that night
To say that my distillery was burning down.
Now I wouldn't say this in public, naturally,
But I felt relieved.
Making gin in Windsor County
Is not my idea of a profitable business.
Do not misunderstand, I am no temperance zealot
Who insists that others should live
As I would have them believe I do.
I like my gin, and my brandy,
And my sling and other mixes just like the next man.
But that distillery always made me feel uneasy.
My partner, Royal Blake, he loved it.
He worked it double hard,
Turning us a small profit from our investment.
Well, anyway, that night, I felt relieved.
So too did old Judge Denison.
He rode out soon as he got word of a fire.
But seeing it was our distillery,
He turned his horse back home, saying he'd have no hand
In putting out that particular conflagration.
I wonder if he was thinking of us, or what we made.
Next morning,
When word spread that so much gin had been lost,
There were a mighty lot of sad hearts in town.
We left the ruins standing there on the hillside,
Sort of a tribute to the gin that might have been.

1829, Dr. Joseph A. Gallup

I know it, dammit, you don't have to tell me!
The whole town is drowning in such talk.
It is all rubbish, and I won't hear any more of it.
When we began classes at the Clinical School of Medicine,
In 1827, the hills were abuzz with this blibberish.
No student of mine has ever been,
Nor ever will be
Found guilty of robbing graves!
Now let us get on with our business.
We need the final approval of the Vermont Medical Society.
To secure it without further hitch,
I propose
That our faculty profess a just abhorrence
Of unlawful and immoral methods
For obtaining subjects for practical anatomy.
Fears against disinterring bodies might raise objections.
So I suggest we lay them to rest, ah, forgive me,
By issuing a faculty declaration to the community
That we will not use, nor permit the use of any human body
That might be disinterred hereabouts.
Rutland? Perhaps.
But not Windsor County.

1829, HARRIET GALLUP

When we moved to Woodstock,
Just before the turn of the century,
Father had already become famous.
He was the first graduate of Dartmouth's medical school.
In 1800, he began his medical practice here,
And he opened the town's first drug store.
Also, he engaged extensively in the merchantile trade.
Because so many people were calling themselves "doctors,"
Without qualification or supervision,
Father helped found the Windsor County Medical Society
In the same year the British attacked the United States.
He helped incorporate the Vermont Medical Society.
He said these organizations could set standards
For the proper recognition of medical doctors.
In 1815, he wrote
Sketches of Epidemic Diseases in the State of Vermont.
Heavens, during the winter of 1813 alone,
Fifty-four Woodstock people died from spotted fever.
Malaria, dysentery, small pox, and typhoid fever,
They all took their tragic toll on the community.
Neighbors, friends, relatives, no one was safe.
Now you understand,
I am very proud of my father.

1829, CHARLES DANA

I know I have been acclaimed
In banking, real estate, business at large.
But I want, nevertheless,
To explain to the community,
Why I resigned as company captain of the calvary.
By the midst of the War of 1812,
My company had not been mustered into service.
Instead, we drilled on parade.
Now, how often can you be seen
Returning each evening,
With only the dust from the parade grounds
To show for your patriotism?
I found it hard to resign, of course.
Seventeen years later,
With the memories of 1812 long forgotten,
I was selected to serve on the committee
That was to "inspect" the Clinical College of Medicine.
Perhaps you heard that in 1829,
Rumors were thick about medical schools and dead bodies.
Well, I was proud to lend my name and effort
To assure the village
That Dr. Gallup's students were not disinterring
Any of our deceased neighbors.
Rumors like that could start another war.

1830, Mrs. Julia Arnold Churchill

I knew it!
When Isaac bought Hoisington's tavern three years ago,
I knew no good would come of it.
Now the entire town is preaching temperance,
And Isaac is being urged to forego
The retailing of spiritous drink.
Buying a tavern
Only three years before temperance sweeps the state,
And himself raised a Baptist.
He should have known better.
Well, he is about to be reduced to selling,
Perhaps milk, or sugared water.
I have a successful business of my own,
A millinery shop he tried so often to get me to give up.
Then, Isaac invested in another newspaper,
The fifth weekly in Woodstock at the same time,
With only 3,000 people in the area.
Well, the HENRY CLAY will get none of my money.
Rather than another newspaper,
He should have invested in coffee beans.
Those temperance people will have to drink something.

1830, Dr. A

Look at it this way, Mrs. Corwin,
I have devoted my entire life to medicine,
And to curing the ailments of the body.
The death of your second son,
And perhaps many others in the county,
Was not caused by anything of this world.
No Maam, it was caused by a creature from hell itself.
However, don't be afraid.
With your help, we can stop it
Before it kills the rest of your family,
Or other folks in the village.
I have consulted with others in the medical society,
And we agree that we must disinter your son's body
And look for signs of the vampire.
Come now, Mrs. Corwin, I know this is hard for you,
But we have no choice.
Your boy is innocent, we know.
But the devil possesses him in the grave.
It is our lives, and yours, or that of the vampire.
Surely you have been a good citizen of Woodstock,
And surely you are concerned for the lives and souls
Of your fellow citizens.
There now, I'll tell them you agreed.
You have been very brave about this, Mrs. Corwin.
We are all in your debt.

1830, MRS. CORWIN

When my second son died,
Of causes unknown to the medical profession,
People began to talk about strange things.
When the doctors in town united in their opinion
That my first son, also dead, was a vampire,
Well, I was outraged.
A vampire? Ridiculous!
Scandalous!
Soon, people began throwing stones through our windows,
And killing our livestock.
Then five of the village doctors came to our house,
Saying the death "was a case of assured vampirism,"
And that they should dig up our older boy
And cook his heart in an iron kettle.
Oh Lord, I was sick from the shock.
But they kept after me, until finally . . .
Well, who was I to deny
Such learned men their opinion?

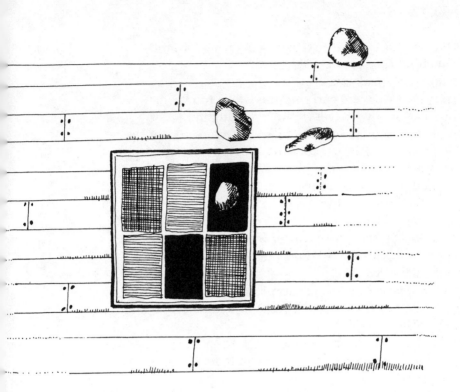

1830, DR. *B*

When our party went to Cushing Burying Ground
That chilly June morn, 1830,
I wanted to speak out,
To say that we were carrying this much too far.
The Corwin boy was no victim of a vampire.
If only the medical school had known more
About tuberculosis, or "consumption" as it is called,
I am sure we would have determined that his death
Resulted from natural causes.
When the other doctors asserted that the first boy
Was a vampire,
I tried to stop the entire matter by saying the opposite.
I contended, instead, that no vampire was at work
While that boy lived.
But I had heard that the fever might be avoided
By burning the heart of a deceased member of the family.
Superstitious? Possibly.
But understand our limitations back in 1830.
The other doctors interpreted my statement
As supporting the vampire claim,
And they embraced me as a brother in the medical society
For confirming their belief.
So there I was,
Forced by my uncertainty to agree.
Well, look at it this way:
How would it look if I called out in single protest?
I have to earn a living in this county.
So, that is why
I joined them that chilly June morn,
In the Cushing Burying Ground.

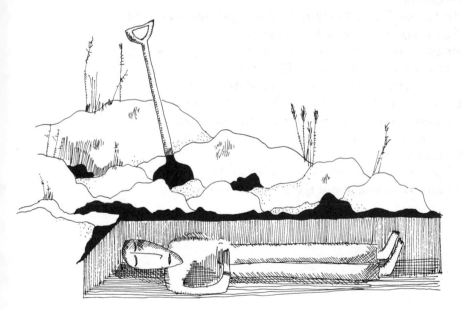

1830, Dr. *C*

"There, look at it, that proves it!
There is still blood in it, six months later.
Surely that proves he is a vampire."
Never in my career have I witnessed such damning proof.
To think it occupied the earthly remains of this boy
And stalked among us at night to do the devil's work!
I tell you, I saw it.
Blood, dripping from a decayed heart.
We of the medical society were right all along.
I had feared that initially,
We might be embarked on treacherous waters.
Our diagnosis might have proven false,
Thereby jeopardizing our professional reputations.
But thank heavens
There was liquid blood in that heart, six months dead
And supposed to be dried to dust.
Proof enough that ours was no hysterical speculation,
But considered, determined judgment,
In line with the expertise we possessed.
By agreement, we boiled the heart in an iron cauldron
And buried it fifteen feet deep in the Common.
We covered it with a seven ton slab of granite,
Quarried from Knox ledge.
Now you understand, this should rid the county
Of any loose talk about the medical society.

1830, CORWIN BOY

As they lifted off the lid,
Through the dried, hollow sockets that had been my eyes,
I could see men dressed in black coats,
With tall black hats.
They peered down at me,
Lying sunken and shriveled under my wool suit.
I glimpsed Mother too, watching, scared, her face pale
Against those hats nodding in somber unison.
Ouch!
Even in death the scalpel hurt my chest.
Soon, my chest cavity, such as was left of it,
Was exposed by the blade.
A hushed gasp arose,
And I saw my own heart being lifted from my grave.
Hell, I was no vampire.
I only died of something the doctors feared
More than they understood.
Others died in 1830, not just me.
Why me?
Dying of tuberculosis was bad enough,
Now this added indignity.
Was it all a painful dream, or a hoax?
But . . . Ouch!
I can still feel that pain.

1830, W. BELL

For June 1830, month of flowers and early growth,
And of licentious behavior in the village,
I thought it appropriate that I print the entire text
Of the sermon delivered by Reverend Fisk,
Of Washington D.C.
After all, Reverend Fisk is not to be taken lightly.
Of great coincidence,
His sermon was devoted to the fires of evil,
"The wicked shall be turned into Hell."
How appropriate then,
At the very time I printed Rev. Fisk's sermon,
That my readers should be exposed
To manifestations of the devil
Visited on us by that poor member
Of the Corwin Family.
Rev. Fisk had no way of knowing
How timely his sermon would be.
And I had no way of knowing
How timely my reporting it would be.
Could this be serendipity,
Or Divine Providence?

1830, MOODY HEATH

This has been a busy year in the village.
Barker's Hotel burned down.
The county jail went up in flames with it,
Along with a horse and a lot of property.
The STANDARD lost its printing plates.
What coverage it was able to give
Was devoted to who held how much insurance from the fire.
All sorts of talk about vampires,
Grown men boiling hearts in cauldrons on the Green.
People dropping dead from the fever.
I tell you,
I am happy to be a humble man,
Content to carve the wooden eagle for the Eagle Hotel.
After I finished it,
I put on a special preservative
To protect it through the years.
I wanted people coming by the hotel,
Long after I was gone,
To see it and maybe think a kind thought about me.
As 1830 ended, I said a prayer
That the hotel would not burn down
For the sake of the owners,
For the sake of the guests,
And for the sake of my eagle.

1830, HARRIET MYRICK

Do not think me ignorant
Of what people say about my sister and me.
Still, we live quietly,
We go to church, are a burden to no one.
We have a perfect right to keep to ourselves if we like.
We love to walk on our lawn and watch people on the Green,
To hear the Revere bells
Summon members of the various religious flocks to prayer,
Woodstock has six churches you know.
Surely that is sufficient for parishioners and ministers
Alike to pray for peace and quiet in the village.
This summer, the village finally leveled the ground
On the Green, and planted it with grass.
I wonder if that is how all that talk
Of burying human hearts in iron pots began.
Thank heavens they took down
Those disgusting whipping blocks,
And the stocks along with them.
Well, at least folks cannot say that my sister and I
Had anything to do with vampires,
Or whipping young boys in the stocks.
We choose to live quietly.
In our village,
Folks are entitled to keep to themselves.

1830, PATTY MYRICK

Harriet and I will undoubtedly die together.
But that does not bother me,
No her.
We believe, fervently,
That the human soul migrates after death
And returns to earth in a different form of life.
So we are happy with our lot in life,
Content to sew our own clothes, and those of others,
Foresaking the frivolities of fashion,
Satisfied with a cup of green tea
And perhaps an egg for dinner.
Our one vice, if you call it that,
Is the enjoyment of yellow snuff,
Which is permitted to the ladies in these times.
We know that when we die, we shall return
To observe and live among our friends,
And among those who are not so friendly.
For you see, the soul never dies.
We will not die.
That is why we never kill spiders
That weave webs in the ceiling corners of our rooms.
They may well be relatives, neighbors,
Or former friends of ours.

1842, SAMUEL WHITNEY

Now and then, the law takes a peculiar turn
And helps us ordinary folk pull one on the lawyers.
Remember how the Woodstock Turnpike Company
Built that bridge over the Ottauquechee,
Just up from my hotel?
Folks used to travel way around it,
Just to avoid paying the toll.
The biggest user of that bridge and the damned toll?
Me, costing me about $30.00 per year
For stage-coach services to my hotel.
So I kept my eyes open and waited.
Finally, the town voted to buy the bridge,
By resolution passed September 6, 1842,
But only if the cost was no more than $50.00.
The owners wouldn't sell at that price.
Just when it looked as if I'd have to go on paying
For the use of that bridge during the rest of my life,
The teamster, Mr. Flint,
Suffered injuries driving between Woodstock and Boston.
He recovered a judgment against the company
And attached the franchise,
Putting it up for sheriff's sale
When the owners wouldn't pay off the judgment.
I showed up at the auction with only two other people.
I kept Doc Gallup's boy from bidding,
And I paid off Flint for his claim,
Then I bought that damned franchise for $3.00.
Well, don't you imagine I was a proud sight the next day,
When I went out to that toll gate
And threw it in the river.

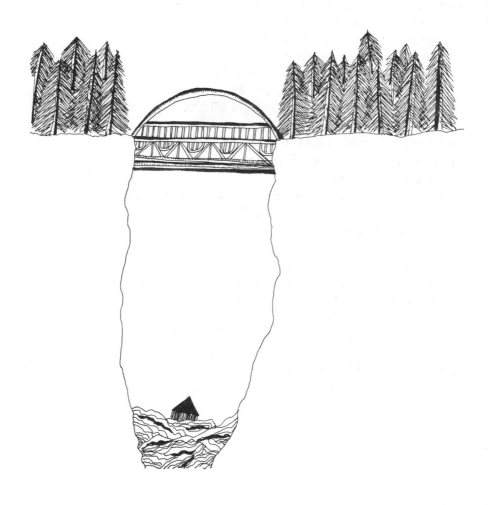

1847, GENERAL TRUMAN BISHOP RANSOM

I believe people remember only
The recent years of your life,
Rather than think of who you were beforehand.
Take me for instance.
I was killed in the Mexican War,
At the Battle of Chapultepec.
Not many people in Vermont cared
If a war was going on in Mexico at the time.
They knew sheep raising was profitable.
They knew that wheat farming had already moved
To the wide, fertile prairies of the midwest.
They thought of lumbering and dairying,
And harnessing power from the rivers for milling.
When news of my death reached Woodstock,
People talked of the distant war, of my "heroic" charge
To the walls of the Chapultepec fortress.
Some remembered me as teaching mathematics
In the military academy at Norwich.
I doubt if anyone knew what came before:
My father dying penniless in 1819,
My paying for an education by playing in the army band,
And my teaching some years in Mississippi
Before returning to Vermont.
What do generals think of
While they lay dying on distant battle fields?
They think of family, of loved ones, of the home town
They will never see again.

1848, FREDERICK BILLINGS

When I journeyed from Vermont to California,
I left behind
Friends, family, a promising public career.
News of the gold rush had stirred in me
The juices of adventure and fortune.
Bezer Simmons told Laura that he planned
To set up a commercial exchange in San Francisco,
The port town for shipment of gold from Sutter's Mill.
When they asked me to join them,
Well, don't you suppose I seized the chance?
I was twenty-six years old,
Already Secretary of Civil and Military Affairs,
Under Governor Eaton.
The family had recovered from its initial poverty
Following our move to Woodstock.
Frankly, I did not want to agonize the rest of my life,
Wondering if I should have joined the gold rush of 1849.
Besides, I did not want to leave my sister
To face a new life alone, 3,000 miles from home.
Bezer was a fine man and all of that,
But Laura was my favorite sister.
On February 1st, with my law shingle packed,
Along with legal texts on contracts, torts and forms,
Laura, Bezer and I set sail on *The Falcon*.
Regrets? . . . Of course.
But wouldn't you have done the same?

1849, LAURA BILLINGS SIMMONS

Bezer, my husband, was a whaling captain.
He purchased property in San Francisco
During one of his trips,
Planning to open a commercial trade
In conjunction with the California gold rush.
Frederick, my younger brother, decided to venture with us
And share in our dream of fame and fortune.
We left New York by ship for the Isthmus of Panama,
A tropical land of swamps and mountains
Which blocked commercial travel
Between the Atlantic and Pacific.
Panama was beset with fever and bugs
And revolutionary outbreaks.
No canal, no railroad, only mule pack, canoes, mosquitoes,
And interminable delays for ship connections at the end.
We crossed safely.
Frederick wrote detailed reports of the passage
Which were printed in THE WOODSTOCK MERCURY.
We sailed nineteen days from Panama to our new home.
On April 1, 1849, my prayers were answered:
We landed in San Francisco.
Frederick was the first lawyer in the city,
Very timely considering all the mining claims to be drafted.
Five days after our arrival,
I fell ill with the Panama fever.
Despite the best medical attention available,
I died, April 24th, and Bezer died one year later.
How ironic,
That we should cause him to travel so far with us,
And then leave him alone,
Away from friends, family,
A promising public career,
To earn the fame and fortune
All of us had dreamed of sharing.

1850, MARY POWERS

To tell the truth,
I did not actually experience the painful
Frontier life of Vermont.
My grand daddy was Dr. Stephen Powers,
The very first doctor to set foot in Woodstock.
Back in 1774, just about anyone who set foot in Woodstock
Was the first something.
But he was special.
He wore buckskin breeches,
And he used to sharpen his operating knives on them.
The sight of him whipping out his cutting knife
And giving it a few licks on the seat of his pants
Must have brought some of his patients
Closer to death than any fever.
Snowshoes and horses,
They were the best means of transportation then,
Depending on the season.
He had it hard back in 1774.
His son, my father, also was a medical doctor.
His life was not as hard, but rigorous enough.
Strange, the first time I experienced real pain
Was the last time.
Despite all of the doctors in my family tree,
I died giving birth to my child.

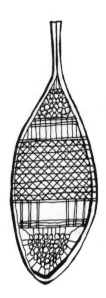

1851, Mrs. Betsy Barrows

When people asked me
Why I did not go along with my husband,
I replied, as pleasantly as I could,
Given the circumstances,
That he only went to sell some horses and property,
And that he planned to return shortly.
When weeks stretched into months, and no word from him,
And when months stretched into years,
Well, naturally I fell prey to the rumors
That he had been murdered, or jailed.
Sure, he'd had eccentric ways about him
When he lived in Bridgewater, later in Woodstock.
But who among us does not?
When the creditors came 'round for payment,
I told them, "He seems to have forgot his debts,
As well as the way back."
Years later, when word came to me
That he was living in New Orleans, with a new wife,
I began entertaining the idea
That he would return to Woodstock, to me.
I'd fix up the house, the one I lived in
Through the generosity of Lawyer Williams,
And imagine extending full welcome to my prodigal mate,
Even to his new woman, if need be.
If only I'd had one last look at him before I died.
Perhaps, perhaps he did forget the way back home.

1854, Mrs. Aseneth Vaughan Darling

Had I lived five months longer,
I would have enjoyed
Both the spectacle and the irony
Of the burning of the Woodstock Courthouse.
It seems that the town's people were on the Green,
Celebrating the glorious Fourth of July.
An enterprising youth,
Swept away with the exhilaration of the festivities,
Threw a firecracker on the roof of the Courthouse.
Now, 1854 will go down in history for two reasons:
I died, at the age of eighty-eight,
And the Courthouse burned, at the age of sixty-three.
It had stood proudly, dispensing justice and order,
Such as we knew it,
Ever since the last courthouse burned.
That was back in 1791,
When they tried to blame poor Cato Boston
For everything that went wrong in the village.
I am not regretting any of my eighty-eight years,
I merely comment
That I would have enjoyed living another five months
To see the Courthouse burned down
By a Fourth of July firecracker.
What an astonishing way of renewing our national ideals.

1856, Susan Powers

Dr. Thomas Powers was really my half-brother.
Daddy remarried after his first wife died.
Thomas was elected to the State House in 1850,
And shortly thereafter was chosen Speaker.
Legislators seemed to spend so much of their time
Debating the issues of the day in taverns,
I don't know if they elected him
Because of his temperance position,
Or in spite of it.
In 1853, He became the first editor
Of THE VERMONT TEMPERANCE STANDARD,
Building up its circulation to 3,000
By the end of the first year.
Must be the temperance men who elected him from Woodstock.
There had to be others with him
Who did not indulge of gin, or brandy, or whiskey.
I had always thought men had to be drinkers to succeed.
Thomas was also one of the founders
Of the Ottauquechee Savings Bank.
He was a pillar of the Woodstock Debating Society,
Refining his gift of gab
Into a valuable weapon for his political speeches.
With all of that talking, and all of that temperance,
And all of that politicking,
No wonder he did not stay in medicine.

1857, DR. THOMAS E. POWERS

True, I loved public office.
I loved the exchange of ideas in social context,
The guiding of governmental policy,
The debate, the competition between disparate groups.
I loved representing the individual
While mollifying the crowd.
I loved the opportunity to persuade my fellow man.
Medicine, yes, it is necessary,
And I am grateful to have learned it,
Particularly at the personal instruction of my father.
But my heart was much more in debate, in commerce,
In attempting to influence public attitudes.
I thrive on the uncertainty of a vote,
Not knowing who will be the winner,
Or the loser,
Until the speeches have been made and the ballots counted.
When I became
The first editor of THE VERMONT TEMPERANCE STANDARD,
I had an opportunity available to so few people:
I had a platform to express, to editorialize
My opinions about taxation, care for the poor,
Finance, taxes, education, the rights of our citizens.
Also, I had an opportunity
To extol the virtues of temperance.

1861, Jacob Collamer

So thick was the hatred
Between men of the South
And the rest of us from the North,
That you could almost cut the dread spectre of war
With a boning knife.
Only a fool could fail to see the tragic consequences
That were to befall our nation.
Being from Vermont, Woodstock in particular,
I represented in the Congress a constituency
That might have thought itself isolated
From events on the Potomac.
But serving as a member of the U.S. Senate
Enabled me to see the pressures on the South to secede,
And the pressures on President Lincoln to prevent it,
And the terrible loss of American lives
That would result.
To think: America, less than one hundred years old
And ready to tear herself apart
Because of greed and pride and regional factionalism.
I saw it coming.
So did most of the leaders of our nation.
Yet, with all of our education, all of our dedication,
All of our compassion and patriotism,
And our greed, pride, and factionalism,
We could do nothing to stop it.
How I grieved for those lives
Years before they were lost.

1861, LT. COLONEL PETER T. WASHBURN

We marched out of town, past the Woodward factory
That early morning, Monday, May 2, 1861,
Through Ludlow and over the hill into Rutland.
I commanded the seventy-six men
In the Woodstock Light Infantry,
Otherwise known as Company B of the First Vermont Regiment.
We had been ordered, along with Company E from Cavendish,
To join the Vermont First in Rutland
And proceed south to Fort Monroe, Virginia,
In defense of the Union.
We arrived May 13th, hot, tired, weary from the blisters,
Poor food, and insect bites all over our bodies.
Fearful and ill-prepared, we came under fire June 10th
At the Battle of Great Bethel.
Captain Bill Pelton was with me,
As were Lts. Andrew Dike and Solomon Woodward.
Reuben Parker was captured.
To be honest, many of our troops were terrified
At seeing the reality of death
Swagger back and forth along our lines in bloody triumph.
Dana Whitney was killed in July,
Somewhere between Newport News and Hamilton,
Towns we had never heard of before the summer.
Odd, I survived the charge at Great Bethel
Only to die in the governor's chair nine years later.

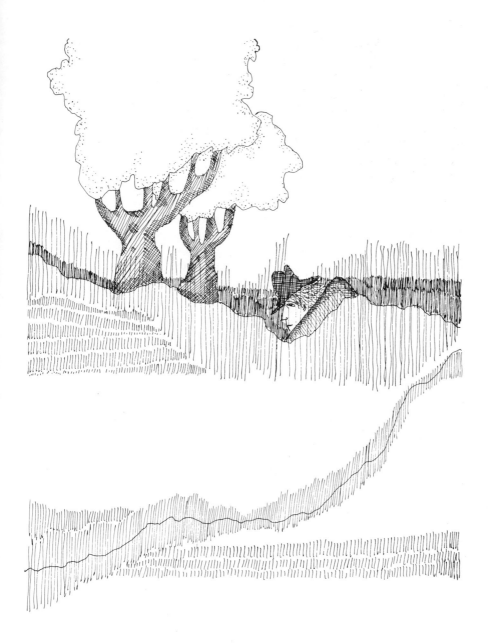

1861, PRIVATE REUBEN M. PARKER

I managed to get myself captured
At the Battle of Big Bethel,
Of "Great" Bethel, depending on your rank.
That was bad enough, getting captured,
Especially after I'd stopped to attend Major Winthrop,
Disguised as a private,
Who, it turned out, had been killed the day before.
My captors took me to Yorktown,
Then to Richmond,
Where I was exchanged for some Rebel prisoners
Taken by the North.
You can imagine my mixed feelings on the whole matter.
There I was, facing death at any moment,
Possibly months or years
In the yet unknown cruelties of Andersonville.
Suddenly, I became the first captured Union soldier
To be exchanged in the Civil War,
A record of two-edged distinction.
Honest, sincere questions were to be asked.
Why did I allow myself to be captured?
Did I try to escape?
How many Reb soldiers was I worth?
Why wasn't I worth more?
Didn't my captors think me dangerous enough to want to keep?
You can understand why I grew quiet about the whole affair.
Now that it is all over, and my name historically recorded,
I wish I had never been captured.

1863, Lt. Henry H. French

Not everyone who dies in battle
Is killed by the enemy.
Take me for instance.
Twenty-one years old,
A promising young officer,
A bright career reportedly
Awaiting my return to Woodstock.
Half way through the Vicksburg Campaign,
January 20, 1863, to be exact,
I died of the fever.
Not that I was the only one sick and dying at the time.
On January 1st,
Over one-third of our 620 men were on the sick list,
Men wounded, men wretching as the heat baked our stomachs,
Men groaning as death rode unchallenged through camp
Day and night.
I wished I could have lived five months more,
Enough to see General Grant beat Pemberton to his knees.
Hell, I wished I'd have kept on living.
My remains were shipped to Woodstock for interment,
A silent, unwilling tribute
To the patriotism burning in Windsor County.
While I lay burning with fever, back near Vicksburg,
The high temperature causing my blood
To race faster through my brain,
I thought how much smarter
The enemy would have been,
To let us alone in those hellish swamps
And boiling forests,
Infested with snakes and leeches,
And bugs of voracious fury.
We'd have all died from exposure,
Thereby leaving the South to win by default.

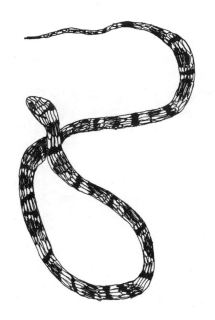

1864, Caroline Crane Marsh

I cannot help it!
They have no right to call my husband
Ill-tempered and opinionated.
He has been: editor, farmer, lawyer, scholar,
Businessman, linguist, politician.
Naturally he should lose patience with dolts
Who drain his time with their babble and self-esteem.
Despite the handicap of my illness
That I brought to his life,
He became the foremost American scholar of our day.
When people criticized his book, *Man and Nature,*
He was quick to point out both the error
Of their logic and the folly of their motives.
Outspoken? A "cranky yankee"? Perhaps.
He was also the founder
Of the conservation movement in America.
While U.S. Minister to Turkey,
Then to Italy,
He was a fearless, brilliant spokesman for America.
On the other hand,
European scholars were reclusive,
Remaining aloof from politics and controversy.
How dull! How unworthy!
Let them emerge from their inconsequential musings.
Let them compete among the learned societies.
Let them earn the right
To call my husband ill-tempered and opinionated.

1864, GEORGE PERKINS MARSH

I have watched man destroy
The natural abundance of our world.
We forget that the earth
Was given to us for our use,
Not for consumption or profligate waste.
But for the tragedy involved,
I would laugh at our efforts to reduce the earth
To an unfit home for her noblest inhabitant.
Animals learn their lessons of survival.
Even the crows of this generation
Are wiser than their ancestors.
Surely mankind should not remain
Essentially a destructive force.
I wrote *Man and Nature* in outrage at such impudence.
My purpose was to make practical suggestions,
Rather than theoretical speculations,
Regarding the preservation of natural resources.
While serving as U.S. Minister to Italy,
I compared the devastation of Mediterranean landscape
To land clearing techniques in Vermont.
There, felling of forests
Brought momentous consequences to the drainage of soil.
I count some success in my life
For having caused so many people to share my revulsion
Of man's callous disregard for the laws of nature.

1867, WILLIAM HEWITT

I do not mean to criticize a hometown paper,
But coverage of the burning of Barker's Hotel
Left a lot to be desired.
First of all,
The report said the jailhouse behind the hotel
Was occupied by "William R. Hewitt, Wholesale Furniture."
That's me, William R. Hewitt.
I can not tell you how many of my customers called on me
To express their regrets that I was in jail.
Dammit, I was not in jail!
My furniture store was leasing space next to the jail.
The blaze began mysteriously
On the second floor of the hotel barn.
It spread to the nearby buildings,
And within three hours, the entire district was reported
To be a smoking ruin.
Happily, I suppose, the jail burned,
And I will not have to endure more ridicule
About my being behind bars.
The account noted one victim,
A horse named "Draco."
The rest of the coverage was devoted
To the amounts of insurance coverage
Carried by the burned out businesses.
Nobody has accused me
Of being involved with excessive insurance coverage.
They all think I was serving time in that damn jail.

1867, LUCY COLLAMER McKENZIE

I am often struck with the ironic reporting of history.
All of Woodstock has been talking about the fire
At Barker's Hotel.
Because the printing plates of THE STANDARD also were burned,
A much smaller newspaper has been appearing.
I have taken to reading the shortened edition
Much more carefully.
For example, the edition of April 4, 1867,
Two weeks after the fire,
Reported that Indians
Had captured Ft. Buford last year, news traveling slowly,
Along the Yellowstone River, on the Upper Missouri,
And that eighty people in the garrison,
Including Colonel Rankin,
His wife and child had been massacred.
No word of what caused the attack
Or the fall of the garrison,
Or why the fort was there in the first place.
Rather than explain all this,
The next column contained an advertisement
For Perry's Moth and Freckle Lotion, $2.00 per bottle.
Is this mingling of news and advertising to imply
That the dead at Ft. Buford would still be alive,
Had they purchased their bottles of Perry's Lotion?
As a reader who holds human life in highest respect,
I feel outraged.

1868, NORMAN WILLIAMS

After admission to practice law in 1814,
I opened my office and began to compete with the likes of
George Marsh, Andrew Tracy, Ben Swan
And other legendaries of the Woodstock bar.
I became State Auditor in 1820, elected for three terms.
Then Secretary of State until 1831.
That marked the peak of my career.
Since 1839, I have held no public office
Higher than clerk of the Windsor County Court.
I helped start THE VERMONT MERCURY,
Which closed shop in 1855.
I was chosen Grand Master of Local Masonic Lodge, No. 23,
But later that night, the faithful chose to close the lodge
Rather "than live in discord
And have fellowship with the unfruitful works of darkness."
I was installed
As the first Secretary of the Agricultural Society
In Windsor County, only to watch it dissolve two years later.
I lectured in Woodstock, at the Vermont Medical School,
Which shut its doors in 1862.
Maybe I possessed the visionary powers of Cassandra.
Now that I think of it,
Before college, I wrote poetry for THE NORTHERN MEMENTO.
That paper folded after only one year.
No one can say my life has been dull.

1868, DR. EDWARD H. WILLIAMS

No matter what success a man might achieve,
People will remember one incident in his life
And use that as the measure of his stature.
How often do people ask me
About the time I tended Phineas Gage.
Phineas by all rights should have been killed in 1848.
A tamping iron was blown through his head,
If you must know,
Into the left cheek and out the top of his skull,
While he was packing dynamite
For the Rutland Railroad, near Cavendish.
I operated on him, and he lived another thirteen years.
I would much rather talk about
The railroad air brakes I introduced.
When a person leaves engineering, becomes a doctor,
Returns to engineering, and emerges as general manager
Of the Pennsylvania Railway System,
Later president of the Baldwin Locomotive Works,
That person is obviously more interested
In railroads than medicine.
I contributed to many philanthropies,
Donated land and funds
For The Norman Williams Memorial Library.
Despite all this,
I will be recorded for saving the life of Phineas Gage.
His skull and the rod are still on display
In the Harvard Medical School Museum.
Just think if Phineas had not gone to work that day.

1872, HIRAM POWERS

I do not understand why they keep insisting
I was a Vermont artist.
Born there?
Yes, but I only lived there as a young child.
I doubt if anyone remembered seeing me in Woodstock.
It was in Ohio that I learned to repair clocks, and
How to structure forms and colors
Into creative expression.
Actually, I found great analogy
Between clocks and sculpture.
The organized, mechanical division of time
Is similar to the structure of lines and form,
Together with the realistic influence of color.
The spatial dimensions of art
Relate to the projected measurement of time,
Or vice versa, whichever.
But I learned all this in Ohio, later in Washington D.C.,
Still later in Florence,
Where I chose to live the remainder of my life.
I wonder if that American minister to Italy,
He was from Woodstock,
Had anything to do with the rumor
That I was a Vermont artist.

1872, GOVERNOR JULIUS CONVERSE

After I arrived in Woodstock,
I began to practice law.
Soon, I represented Bethel, and later Windsor County
In the state legislature.
Shortly thereafter,
I was elected Attorney General for the state.
Through it all, my wife and I remained childless.
I know the rigors of childbirth
Threatened the life of every mother-to-be.
Still, as I grew older,
I wanted progeny to carry on the family heritage.
Half-way through the century,
I served a term as Lt. Governor.
After my first wife died, I remarried.
By only one vote, I beat out Fred Billings
For nomination as Governor.
Admittedly his own campaign manager
Swung a number of votes to me.
Yes sir, 1872 has been a good year to me.
I married the young and beautiful Jane Martin,
And I won the nomination for governor.
Who says life cannot begin at seventy-five?

1873, MRS. JANE MARTIN CONVERSE

Fairy tales do come true.
Let me tell you from personal experience,
They do come true.
When Governor Converse proposed to me,
I knew that I was living in a fairy tale.
I had read about him in school,
Been taught what a fine example of honor and dedication
He was, and I cheered for him during his campaign,
And celebrated with him at the convention
Where he won the nomination for governor.
I grieved with the rest of the state when his wife died,
And lamented that he, given his advanced age,
Would be left childless,
Much to the loss of Vermont.
So you can imagine the conflict in my heart
When, at age seventy-five, he proposed to me.
I told myself,
"Because he wants to share the remainder of his days with me,
I will be proud and honored
To share to the fullest extent, my life with him."
So I did, and he did,
And Luna Belle was born thirteen months later.

1874, Luna Belle Converse

People could not believe the news,
When Mother announced that she
Was pregnant with me.
Daddy had been a teacher, a lawyer, a state senator,
Governor of Vermont.
Despite all of these successes,
He was seventy-six years old.
Strange that his first wife,
After living with him forty-five years,
Should die childless,
When after only one year married to Mother,
He should father me.
I remember so well,
He would play with me, hold me on his knee
And talk to me of life and politics and law.
I would bounce and laugh, and sometimes cry.
He would dry my eyes, talk to me,
And soon turn my childish tears into laughter.
I asked him directly why he chose to become a father
So late in life.
He replied that he loved my mother very much,
And that he loved me very much, also.
That was answer enough for me.

1875, Frederick Billings

Alone in San Francisco,
Following the tragic death of Laura,
Then Bezer Simmons,
I plunged into the practice of law, mining claims,
Everything that could bring the fortune and success
We had dreamed of sharing.
Soon, I repaid with generous interest
The $1,000 loan advanced by Al Catlin
To finance my trip westward.
I helped keep California in the anti-slavery bloc,
Denouncing the evils of slavery
And the suspicious motives of its advocates.
I helped to found the University of California,
Became president of the Northern Pacific Railroad.
Yes, by all standards I prospered.
Also, I married and began to raise a family.
With achievements, honors, struggles, love,
My fortune made and my health shattered,
I returned to Vermont to die
Fifteen years later.
I must say,
The practice of law
Is more lucrative out of state.

1875, GEORGE WESTON

When Mr. Billings bought the old Charles Marsh farm,
Just north of the Ottauquechee,
He hired me to manage things.
I knew good cattle,
And I knew how to run a good farm.
We started with two hundred and fifty acres,
And before long, he owned up to two thousand.
If not the biggest farm in New England,
It certainly was the best.
We built up a herd of Jersey cows.
Beautiful creatures they were,
Imported straight from the Isle of Jersey.
By judicious breeding,
And the best of care and feeding
Over the long winters,
Mr. Billings and me,
We produced the finest Jersey herd in the nation.
He certainly was a wonder to work for.
Always knowledgeable of what was going on
And what to do about it.
Haying, planting, dairying, buying land, grain markets,
He was expert in all of them.
I tell you, I knew good cattle.
And Mr. Billings, he knew good men.
He hired me, didn't he?

1875, Mrs. Julia Parmly Billings

My husband had a flair for business,
A gift for architecture, a genius for finance.
He was a brilliant public speaker.
But, oh what a humble beginning he had.
When he first arrived in Woodstock,
He drove the family hog behind the wagon.
Little wonder he vowed he would never be poor again.
I cannot blame him for that.
He would work day and night,
And would happily share his wealth with family,
Community, employees.
Upon his return to Woodstock, wealthy and reknown,
Mr. Billings continued his exhausting pace,
Serving as president of the Woodstock Railroad,
President of the Woodstock National Bank,
Heavily involved with the town's charities.
Years later, with so much accomplished,
And so much more he wanted to do,
He died.
The town, the state and the nation
Mourned his passing.
Yes indeed,
The Lord gave my husband ten talents,
And he used them to the fullest.

1875, Mr. Liberty Bates Marbles

In 1875, the Woodstock Railroad embarked on its first trip,
Crossing the fourteen miles
From Woodstock to White River Junction without mishap.
It did not seem hardly worth while,
To build a train just to run from Woodstock
To White River Junction, or even the other way around.
Folks have been traveling between Woodstock
And White River Junction by horse as long as I remember.
Didn't need a train to take them.
Actually, it was built to carry quality folk
Direct from New York and Boston to Woodstock.
They wouldn't have to sully their feet in White River.
The biggest thing about it was the bridge over the gorge,
Built to keep the engine and cars,
And the people in them,
From plunging 163 feet
Into the roaring Quechee waters below.
The engine had to puff and spin its way up Shallies Hill,
Scrabbling like a bull on lard
Whenever snow fell on the tracks.
Sheer folly, the whole thing.
Someday, someone's going to grease those rails,
And that train's going to slide
All the way back to town.
That's when I'll be glad I stayed home.

1877, Solomon Woodward

When we arrived in Woodstock,
I was determined to operate the mill successfully,
And profitably.
Through long hours, hard work,
All of my personal strength,
And the men working hours after most others would quit,
We repaired the building
And had it ready to open January 1st, 1848.
The repairs took six long months.
In recompense for the loneliness and anxiety
I inflicted upon my wife during those long months,
I built her a mansion on Mountain Avenue,
A beautiful structure, one worthy of her patience.
Then, I suppose it had to happen,
Although, like one's own death,
It appears unexpectedly,
Double tragedy struck me.
My beloved wife died,
And a depression forced the closing of my mill.
Success does not strengthen a man against tragedy,
Or failure,
It makes him more vulnerable.

Bibliography

1. *History of Windsor County,* edited by Lewis Cass Aldrich and Frank R. Holmes. D. Mason & Co., N.Y. 1891.

2. THE VERMONT STANDARD, Woodstock, Vermont, pre-1876.

3. *History of Woodstock, Vermont,* by Henry Swan Dana. Houghton, Mifflin & Co., Boston & N.Y., 1889.

4. *Encyclopedia of Vermont Biography,* ed. by Prentiss C. Dodge. Ullery Publishing Co., Burlington, Vt., 1912.

5. *Woodstock, Vermont,* by Henry Boynton. Woodstock Library document (No. 080 B71).

6. *History of Vermont,* by Walter Hill Crockett, Vols. I-V. The Century House Co., Inc., N.Y., 1923.

7. *Vermont in the Civil War,* by G.G. Benedict, Vol. II. The Free Press Association, Burlington, Vt., 1886.

8. *Morgan Horses,* by D.C. Linsley. C.M. Saxton, Barker & Co., N.Y., 1856.

9. *Woodstock Now & Then,* by Rhoda Teagle. The Elm Tree Press, Woodstock, Vt., 1957.

10. *Mischief in the Mountains,* edited by Walter R. Hard, Jr. & Janet C. Greene. Montpelier, 1971.

11. *Early History of Woodstock, Vermont,* by Edward H. Williams, Jr. Brown & Moore, Woodstock, Vermont, 1907.

12. *Man And Nature,* by George P. Marsh. The Balknap Press, Cambridge, Mass., 1865.

13. *George Perkins Marsh: Versatile Vermonter,* by David Lowenthal.

14. THE WOODSTOCK MERCURY, edited by Nahum Haskell, May 20, 1848; May 18, 1849; June 29, 1849. Woodstock, Vermont.

15. *The Edward H. Williams Collection of Japanese Art,* by John H. McDill. The Norman Williams Public Library, Woodstock.

16. *Collier's Encyclopedia,* Louis Shores, Editor-in-chief. Crowell-Collier Educational Corp., N.Y., 1969.

17. *Williard Geneology,* edited by Charles Henry Pope. Murray & Emery Co., Kendall Square, Cambridge, 1915.